Unwin Studies in Physics and Applied Mathematics

Edited by

JOHN M. CHARAP, B.A., M.A., PH.D.

Reader in Theoretical Physics
Queen Mary College
University of London

No. 3

VECTOR ANALYSIS

by the same author

AN INTRODUCTION TO RELATIVITY (Longmans)

Unwin Studies in Physics and Applied Mathematics

No. 1 DIGITAL SYSTEMS LOGIC AND CIRCUITS
B. Zacharov
Daresbury Nuclear Physics Laboratory

No. 2 QUANTUM MECHANICS: AN INTRODUCTION
J. G. Taylor
University of Southampton

in preparation

ELECTROMAGNETISM (2 vols.)
F. F. Heymann
University College, London

SCATTERING THEORY
S. Zienau
University College, London

VECTOR ANALYSIS

by L. Marder

Senior Lecturer in Mathematics
University of Southampton

London. GEORGE ALLEN AND UNWIN LTD

PRINTED IN GREAT BRITAIN
in 10 on 12pt Times Roman
BY WILLMER BROTHERS LIMITED
BIRKENHEAD

PREFACE

This introductory text on vector algebra and field theory is designed to cover the material normally met by first year undergraduate students of mathematics, physics and chemistry, and of first and second year engineering and applied science students. While the treatment is practical rather than formally rigorous, the main conditions under which theorems and identities are valid are carefully stated. Differential notation is used throughout. Since exact equations in differentials are often confused with corresponding approximations involving small increments, a brief appendix on differentials is included.

Particular features of the book are twofold. Firstly, an attempt is made to motivate the study of the mathematical theory by means of physical illustrations *at each stage*, and not merely at the conclusion of a substantial body of mathematics. It is not, of course, an intention to teach physical theories in this book on vector analysis, and the illustrative material is therefore quite brief. Concepts such as surface and volume integrals of a vector point function are related to physical examples as soon as they are introduced, and Poisson's equation in electrostatics is derived as an application at an appropriate stage. Secondly, in order to develop confidence in the student, a fairly generous number of solved problems is provided. Some of these are entirely straightforward and serve to clarify definitions; others highlight various techniques.

For reasons of space, tensors are not discussed. I believe that these are best treated in books *devoted* to a study of tensors or their applications. Condensed accounts are of necessity rather formal, and not infrequently the reader concludes that tensors are primarily used in connection with vector identities.

The first two chapters are concerned with what is usually called vector algebra, and the rest with vector field theory. Gauss's, Green's and Stokes's integral theorems are covered in chapters 6 to 8, and are used to construct the electrostatic field equations and to discuss the uniqueness of solutions of Poisson's equation. The existence of scalar and vector potentials is dealt with in chapter 9, curvilinear coordinates in chapter 10, and a convenient reference summary of formulae is to be found in chapter 11. Adequate exercises are included at the ends of chapters; answers are given at the end of the book.

L.M.

University of Southampton
1969

CONTENTS

CHAPTER 1

Vector Algebra

1.1 Definitions

The simplest type of quantity we meet in physics has magnitude but no associated direction in space. Examples are mass, temperature, distance and time, and each is specified by (i) an appropriate choice of unit, and (ii) a real number called the *measure*, which is the ratio of the given quantity to this unit. Quantities of this type are called *scalars*, and the algebra of scalars is the ordinary algebra of real numbers applied to the measures. The real numbers themselves are scalars.

The next simplest type of physical quantity has both magnitude (which can always be taken positive) and an associated direction. For example, displacement, velocity, force and momentum are all of this type, and need (i) and (ii), as above, for their specification together with (iii) a statement of the direction. We call these quantities *vectors*. The algebra of vectors consists of a set of rules for manipulating scalars and vectors jointly, in accordance with certain definitions of addition, subtraction, multiplication and division. Each definition is chosen simply by the criterion of what is most useful in practice.

Once the choice of unit has been made, a vector is just a positive number, known as the *magnitude* or *module*, and a direction. This means that a vector can always be represented as a displacement from any chosen *initial point O* to a *terminal point P*, such that the distance OP is the magnitude of the vector, and the direction from O to P is its direction.

The displacement vector from O to P is denoted by $\overrightarrow{OP}$, and on a diagram we indicate the sense of direction by an arrow. In Fig. 1.1, OP and AQ are parallel line segments which are equal in length, and so $\overrightarrow{OP}$ and $\overrightarrow{AQ}$ represent the same vector. It is immaterial where the initial point of a vector is located, and the initial point may be moved at will without

11

changing the vector, provided that the magnitude and direction of the displacement are not changed. To emphasize this, the term *free vector* is often used.

Since $\overrightarrow{OP}$ can be used to indicate the position of P relative to the chosen point O, we call $\overrightarrow{OP}$ the *position vector* of P relative to O.

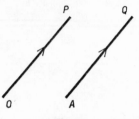

Fig. 1.1

In print, except when it is regarded explicitly as a displacement $\overrightarrow{OP}$, $\overrightarrow{AQ}$, etc., a vector is almost always denoted by bold (Clarendon) type, thus: **a** or **A**, while the corresponding magnitude is denoted by $|\mathbf{a}|$ or $|\mathbf{A}|$ or, if no confusion is likely, by a or A. (In manuscript, a bar below or above a symbol is used to denote a vector quantity: $\underline{a}$, $\bar{a}$, $\underline{A}$, $\bar{A}$, etc.)

Two vectors are said to be *equal* if they have the same magnitude and the same direction. This is indicated by writing $\mathbf{a} = \mathbf{b}$, or $\overrightarrow{OP} = \overrightarrow{AQ}$. If vectors **a** and **b** have the same magnitude but opposite directions, then each is the *negative* of the other. In Fig. 1.2, **b** is the negative of **a**, written $\mathbf{b} = -\mathbf{a}$ or $\mathbf{a} = -\mathbf{b}$.

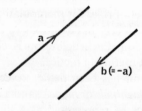

Fig. 1.2

The *zero vector* is any vector of zero magnitude, all zero vectors being equal by definition. The zero vector is denoted by 0 (not bold).

1.2   Addition and Subtraction of Vectors

When two displacements from O to P and from P to Q are made in turn, the resultant displacement is from O to Q, and is called the *sum* of

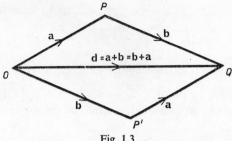

Fig. 1.3

the two displacements. The addition of vectors is defined to be in accord with this rule. Let **a**, **b** be any two vectors (Fig. 1.3) and let O, P and Q be such that $\overrightarrow{OP} = \mathbf{a}$, $\overrightarrow{PQ} = \mathbf{b}$. Then the *sum* or *resultant* of **a** and **b** is defined to be the vector $\mathbf{d} = \overrightarrow{OQ}$, written

$$\mathbf{d} = \mathbf{a} + \mathbf{b}.$$

This definition is known as the *triangle law of addition*, and is often regarded as part of the definition of a vector.

From the parallelogram of Fig. 1.3 it is clear that

$$\mathbf{a} + \mathbf{b} = \mathbf{b} + \mathbf{a},$$

since the right hand side is

$$\mathbf{b} + \mathbf{a} = \overrightarrow{OP'} + \overrightarrow{P'Q} = \overrightarrow{OQ} = \mathbf{a} + \mathbf{b}.$$

We see also that the resultant of two vectors is constructed using the same parallelogram rule as applies to the resultant of two forces in mechanics. When a third vector **c** is added to $\mathbf{a} + \mathbf{b}$, we have that

$$(\mathbf{a} + \mathbf{b}) + \mathbf{c} = \mathbf{a} + (\mathbf{b} + \mathbf{c}),$$

as is evident from Fig. 1.4. Thus, without ambiguity, we can write $\mathbf{a} + \mathbf{b} + \mathbf{c}$ for the sum of the three vectors, where the order in which the vectors appear is immaterial. This result generalizes to any number of vectors.

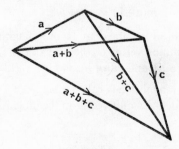

Fig. 1.4

Exercise. If a polygon has n vertices $A_1, A_2, \ldots, A_n$, show that

$$\overrightarrow{A_1 A_2} + \overrightarrow{A_2 A_3} + \ldots + \overrightarrow{A_{n-1} A_n} + \overrightarrow{A_n A_1} = 0.$$

Vector *subtraction* is defined by the statement that $\mathbf{a} - \mathbf{b}$ is to denote the vector $\mathbf{a} + (-\mathbf{b})$. In Fig. 1.5, $\overrightarrow{OP} = \mathbf{a}$, $\overrightarrow{OQ} = \mathbf{b}$ and $\overrightarrow{QP} = \overrightarrow{QO} + \overrightarrow{OP}$ $= (-\mathbf{b}) + \mathbf{a} = \mathbf{a} + (-\mathbf{b}) = \mathbf{a} - \mathbf{b}$. It is clear that for any vector $\mathbf{a}$, we have $\mathbf{a} - \mathbf{a} = \mathbf{a} + (-\mathbf{a}) = 0$.

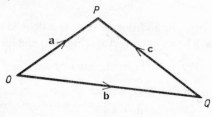

Fig. 1.5

1.3   Multiplication of a Vector by a Scalar

If r vectors $\mathbf{a}$ are added together, where r is a positive integer, the resultant vector is denoted by $r\mathbf{a}$. More generally, if m is any positive real number or zero, then $m\mathbf{a}$ is defined to be the vector whose direction is that of $\mathbf{a}$ and whose magnitude is m times that of $\mathbf{a}$. If m is a negative real number, then $m\mathbf{a}$ is defined to be $-|m|\mathbf{a}$.

It is evident that if m and n are real numbers, then

$$m(n\mathbf{a}) = (mn)\mathbf{a}$$

and

$$(m+n)\mathbf{a} = m\mathbf{a} + n\mathbf{a}.$$

Further, for any real number m and any two vectors $\mathbf{a}$ and $\mathbf{b}$, we have

$$m(\mathbf{a}+\mathbf{b}) = m\mathbf{a} + m\mathbf{b}.$$

The proof of this relation is immediate from a diagram of two similar triangles sharing a common vertex O, the sides drawn from O representing the vectors $\mathbf{a}$, $m\mathbf{a}$, $\mathbf{a} + \mathbf{b}$ and $m(\mathbf{a}+\mathbf{b})$.

Any vector of unit magnitude is called a *unit vector*. Given any non-zero vector $\mathbf{a}$, we can define a unit vector in the direction of $\mathbf{a}$, written $\hat{\mathbf{a}}$. Thus,

$$\hat{\mathbf{a}} = \frac{1}{a}\mathbf{a}, \quad \text{or} \quad \mathbf{a} = a\hat{\mathbf{a}}.$$

1.4   Summary of Algebraic Laws

The algebraic laws obtained so far may be summarized as follows:

$$\text{(i)}\quad \mathbf{a}+\mathbf{b} = \mathbf{b}+\mathbf{a},$$
$$\text{(ii)}\quad (\mathbf{a}+\mathbf{b})+\mathbf{c} = \mathbf{a}+(\mathbf{b}+\mathbf{c}),$$
$$\text{(iii)}\quad m(n\mathbf{a}) = (mn)\mathbf{a},$$
$$\text{(iv)}\quad (m+n)\mathbf{a} = m\mathbf{a}+n\mathbf{a},$$
$$\text{(v)}\quad m(\mathbf{a}+\mathbf{b}) = m\mathbf{a}+m\mathbf{b},$$

where $\mathbf{a}, \mathbf{b}, \mathbf{c}$ are any three vectors, and m, n are scalars (real numbers). The law (i) is called the *commutative* law of addition, (ii) and (iii) are the *associative* laws of addition and multiplication (by a scalar) respectively and (iv), (v) are each forms of *distributive* laws.

1.5   Components of a Vector

Let two vectors $\mathbf{a}$ and $\mathbf{b}$ which are not parallel (in the same or opposite senses) be drawn from the same initial point O. Then they will lie in a definite plane through O. If a third vector $\mathbf{c}$, also drawn from O, lies in the same plane, then the three vectors are said to be *coplanar*. In general, three vectors are coplanar when all are parallel to a plane.

A given vector $\mathbf{r}$ can always be expressed as the sum of three vectors in any three given non-coplanar directions. For, if the given directions are those specified by vectors $\mathbf{a}$, $\mathbf{b}$, $\mathbf{c}$, then a parallelepiped can be constructed with diagonal OP, where $\overrightarrow{OP} = \mathbf{r}$, such that the edges through O are parallel to $\mathbf{a}$, $\mathbf{b}$ and $\mathbf{c}$ respectively (Fig. 1.6). For certain uniquely determined real numbers l, m, n, we shall have $\overrightarrow{OA} = l\mathbf{a}$, $\overrightarrow{OB} = m\mathbf{b}$, $\overrightarrow{OC} = n\mathbf{c}$, and so

$$\mathbf{r} = l\mathbf{a}+m\mathbf{b}+n\mathbf{c}.$$

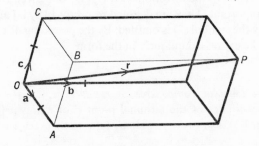

Fig. 1.6

When **a**, **b**, **c** are *unit* vectors, the numbers l, m, n are called the *components* of **r** in the given directions. Some authors use the term components to denote the vectors *l***a**, *m***b**, *n***c**, but we shall refer to these as the *vector components* of **r** in the respective directions.

Let $Oxyz$ be a set of rectangular cartesian coordinate axes (Fig. 1.7). If Oy and Oz are in the plane of the paper, while Ox is directed out of the plane towards the reader, then the system of axes is called *right handed*. In this case a right handed corkscrew directed along Oz, with its handle in the xy plane, will move in the direction Oz when the handle is rotated in the same sense as the 90° rotation taking Ox into Oy. If any

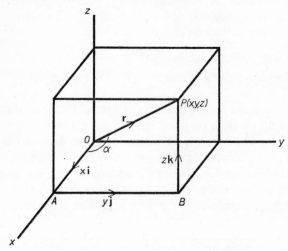

Fig. 1.7

one of the coordinate axes of a right handed system has its direction reversed, then the new system is called *left handed*. We shall be concerned only with right handed systems.

The unit vectors in the directions Ox, Oy, Oz of a given right handed system are important. They are denoted respectively by **i**, **j** and **k**, where for simplicity the symbol (^) is omitted. By the preceding discussion, any vector **r** can be expressed uniquely in the form

$$\mathbf{r} = x\mathbf{i} + y\mathbf{j} + z\mathbf{k}, \tag{1.1}$$

where the *rectangular components* or *resolutes* x, y, z are simply the cartesian coordinates of the terminal point P of **r** drawn from initial point O (Fig. 1.7). For brevity, we may refer to this vector as the vector (x, y, z).

Suppose that the angles made by $\overrightarrow{OP}$ with Ox, Oy and Oz are α, β and γ

respectively. Then $\cos\alpha, \cos\beta$ and $\cos\gamma$ are called the *direction cosines* of **r**. They may be positive, zero or negative and serve to specify the direction of **r**, but not its magnitude. Note that by resolving, we have

$$x = r\cos\alpha, \qquad y = r\cos\beta, \qquad z = r\cos\gamma, \qquad (1.2)$$

and so by (1.1)

$$\hat{\mathbf{r}} = \frac{1}{r}\mathbf{r} = \cos\alpha\,\mathbf{i} + \cos\beta\,\mathbf{j} + \cos\gamma\,\mathbf{k}, \qquad (1.3)$$

which shows that the direction cosines of **r** are the components of the unit vector $\hat{\mathbf{r}}$. Since

$$OP^2 = OA^2 + AB^2 + BP^2,$$

therefore

$$r^2 = x^2 + y^2 + z^2, \qquad (1.4)$$

which shows that the square of the magnitude of a vector is the sum of the squares of its rectangular components. Furthermore, by substituting in (1.4) for x, y, z from (1.2), we have

$$\cos^2\alpha + \cos^2\beta + \cos^2\gamma = 1, \qquad (1.5)$$

which shows that the three direction cosines of a vector are not independent quantities.

By application of the algebraic laws of §1.4, it follows that if $\mathbf{r} = x\mathbf{i} + y\mathbf{j} + z\mathbf{k}$ and $\mathbf{r}' = x'\mathbf{i} + y'\mathbf{j} + z'\mathbf{k}$ are any two vectors, then

$$\mathbf{r} + \mathbf{r}' = (x+x')\mathbf{i} + (y+y')\mathbf{j} + (z+z')\mathbf{k},$$

with a corresponding result for $\mathbf{r} - \mathbf{r}'$. Therefore, to add or subtract vectors expressed in component form we add or subtract the corresponding components.

Example (i). If P and Q are the points with cartesian coordinates $(2, 0, 3)$ and $(1, 4, -1)$, respectively, what are the position vectors of P and Q relative to O, and the position vector of Q relative to P? Determine the magnitude and the direction cosines of $\overrightarrow{PQ}$, and give the angle between the vector $\overrightarrow{PQ}$ and the line Ox.

By definition, the position vectors of P and Q relative to O are

$$\overrightarrow{OP} = 2\mathbf{i} + 3\mathbf{k}, \qquad \overrightarrow{OQ} = \mathbf{i} + 4\mathbf{j} - \mathbf{k},$$

and the position vector of Q relative to P is

$$\overrightarrow{PQ} = \overrightarrow{OQ} - \overrightarrow{OP} = \mathbf{i} + 4\mathbf{j} - \mathbf{k} - (2\mathbf{i} + 3\mathbf{k})$$
$$= -\mathbf{i} + 4\mathbf{j} - 4\mathbf{k}.$$

B

Now,

$$|\overrightarrow{PQ}| = \sqrt{\{(-1)^2+4^2+(-4)^2\}} = \sqrt{33}$$

(the same as the distance PQ). The unit vector in the direction $\overrightarrow{PQ}$ is

$$\overrightarrow{\hat{PQ}} = \frac{1}{\sqrt{33}}(-\mathbf{i}+4\mathbf{j}-4\mathbf{k}),$$

and so the direction cosines of $\overrightarrow{PQ}$ are

$$-\frac{1}{\sqrt{33}}, \frac{4}{\sqrt{33}}, \frac{-4}{\sqrt{33}}.$$

The angle between $\overrightarrow{PQ}$ and Ox is α, where $\cos\alpha = -1/\sqrt{33}$, whence

$$\alpha = 180° - 79°59' = 100°01'.$$

Example (ii). Express, in vector form, the equation of the straight line which passes through the point with position vector $\mathbf{a}$ relative to the origin and is parallel to a given vector $\mathbf{b}$. Determine the equation of the line PQ in the last example, and find the position vector relative to O of the point T which divides PQ internally in the ratio $2:1$.

The vector equation of a straight line is the equation satisfied by the position vector $\mathbf{r}$ of a general point R on the line. By Fig. 1.8, since $\mathbf{r}-\mathbf{a}$ is a multiple of $\mathbf{b}$ for just those points R which lie on the line, the required equation is

$$\mathbf{r}-\mathbf{a} = s\mathbf{b}, \quad \text{i.e. } \mathbf{r} = \mathbf{a}+s\mathbf{b}, \qquad -\infty < s < \infty, \qquad (1.6)$$

where s is a parameter.

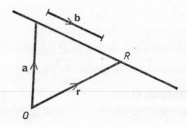

Fig. 1.8

Note: By writing the vectors $\mathbf{r}, \mathbf{a}, \mathbf{b}$ in component form, $\mathbf{r} = (x, y, z)$, $\mathbf{a} = (a_1, a_2, a_3)$, $\mathbf{b} = (b_1, b_2, b_3)$, we get from (1.6)

$$x = a_1+sb_1, \quad y = a_2+sb_2, \quad z = a_3+sb_3,$$

or, on eliminating s,

$$\frac{x-a_1}{b_1} = \frac{y-a_2}{b_2} = \frac{z-a_3}{b_3},$$

which constitute the equations of the line in standard cartesian coordinate form.

Let $\mathbf{a} = \overrightarrow{OP}$, $\mathbf{b} = \overrightarrow{PQ}$. Then, by substituting the expressions found for these vectors into (1.6), we get for the line PQ the equation

$$\mathbf{r} = 2\mathbf{i} + 3\mathbf{k} + s(-\mathbf{i} + 4\mathbf{j} - 4\mathbf{k})$$

$$= (2-s)\mathbf{i} + 4s\mathbf{j} + (3-4s)\mathbf{k}. \qquad (1.7)$$

The given point T is such that $\overrightarrow{PT} = \frac{2}{3}\overrightarrow{PQ}$, and so $\overrightarrow{OT}$ is given by $\mathbf{r}$ in (1.7) when s is put equal to $\frac{2}{3}$. Thus,

$$\overrightarrow{OT} = \frac{4}{3}\mathbf{i} + \frac{8}{3}\mathbf{j} + \frac{1}{3}\mathbf{k} = \frac{1}{3}(4\mathbf{i} + 8\mathbf{j} + \mathbf{k}).$$

1.6 The Scalar Product

When two vectors occur jointly in an application, the product of their magnitudes multiplied by the cosine of the angle between their directions is often of major importance. For example, when the point of application of a constant force $\mathbf{F}$ moves through a displacement $\mathbf{d}$ where $\mathbf{F}$ and $\mathbf{d}$ are inclined at angle θ, the work done by the force is $(F\cos\theta)d = Fd\cos\theta$. This consideration leads to the following definition for the *scalar product* (or *dot product*) of two vectors $\mathbf{a}$ and $\mathbf{b}$ whose directions are inclined at angle θ,

$$\mathbf{a} \cdot \mathbf{b} = ab\cos\theta. \qquad (0 \leqslant \theta \leqslant \pi) \qquad (1.8)$$

Note that scalar multiplication is commutative, i.e. $\mathbf{a} \cdot \mathbf{b} = \mathbf{b} \cdot \mathbf{a}$, and that, as implied by its name, this product of two vectors is itself a scalar, not a vector.

Clearly, by (1.8), for any two vectors $\mathbf{a}$ and $\mathbf{b}$, and real number m, we have the rule

$$(m\mathbf{a}) \cdot \mathbf{b} = m(\mathbf{a} \cdot \mathbf{b}) = \mathbf{a} \cdot (m\mathbf{b}).$$

If $\mathbf{a}$ and $\mathbf{b}$ are mutually perpendicular, then $\cos\theta = 0$ in (1.8) and so $\mathbf{a} \cdot \mathbf{b} = 0$. Another special case occurs when $\mathbf{a}$ and $\mathbf{b}$ have the same direction, giving $\mathbf{a} \cdot \mathbf{b} = ab$, and in particular $\mathbf{a} \cdot \mathbf{a} = a^2$ for any vector $\mathbf{a}$. The latter is also written $\mathbf{a}^2$.

For the unit vectors $\mathbf{i}, \mathbf{j}, \mathbf{k}$, we evidently have

$$\mathbf{i}.\mathbf{i} = \mathbf{j}.\mathbf{j} = \mathbf{k}.\mathbf{k} = 1,$$

$$\mathbf{i}.\mathbf{j} = \mathbf{j}.\mathbf{i} = \mathbf{j}.\mathbf{k} = \mathbf{k}.\mathbf{j} = \mathbf{k}.\mathbf{i} = \mathbf{i}.\mathbf{k} = 0. \tag{1.9}$$

Finally, the distributive laws

$$(\mathbf{a}+\mathbf{b}).\mathbf{c} = \mathbf{a}.\mathbf{c}+\mathbf{b}.\mathbf{c}, \qquad \mathbf{a}.(\mathbf{b}+\mathbf{c}) = \mathbf{a}.\mathbf{b}+\mathbf{a}.\mathbf{c}, \tag{1.10}$$

are valid for general vectors $\mathbf{a}, \mathbf{b}$ and $\mathbf{c}$. It is sufficient to prove the first of these, because the second follows as a consequence of the first and the fact that scalar multiplication is commutative. In Fig. 1.9, AA' and BB' are perpendicular to OC. Thus, if $\overrightarrow{OA} = \mathbf{a}$, $\overrightarrow{AB} = \mathbf{b}$, and $\overrightarrow{OC} = \mathbf{c}$, we have

$$\mathbf{a}.\mathbf{c} = OA'.OC, \qquad \mathbf{b}.\mathbf{c} = A'B'.OC,$$

$$(\mathbf{a}+\mathbf{b}).\mathbf{c} = OB'.OC,$$

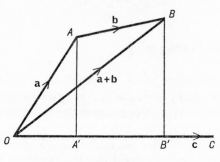

Fig. 1.9

whence the required relation follows since $OB' = OA'+A'B'$.

Repeated use of the above laws enables us to prove that for any two vectors $\mathbf{a} = a_1\mathbf{i}+a_2\mathbf{j}+a_3\mathbf{k}$, $\mathbf{b} = b_1\mathbf{i}+b_2\mathbf{j}+b_3\mathbf{k}$,

$$\mathbf{a}.\mathbf{b} = (a_1\mathbf{i}+a_2\mathbf{j}+a_3\mathbf{k}).(b_1\mathbf{i}+b_2\mathbf{j}+b_3\mathbf{k})$$
$$= a_1 b_1+a_2 b_2+a_3 b_3, \tag{1.11}$$

on evaluating all the products.

Example (i). Find the angle between the vectors $\mathbf{a} = 2\mathbf{i}+2\mathbf{j}-\mathbf{k}$, $\mathbf{b} = \mathbf{i}-\mathbf{j}+3\mathbf{k}$.

We have

$$\mathbf{a}.\mathbf{b} = 2\times1+2(-1)+(-1)3 = -3 = ab\cos\theta,$$

where θ is the required angle. But, by inspection, $a^2 = \mathbf{a} \cdot \mathbf{a} = 9$, $b^2 = \mathbf{b} \cdot \mathbf{b} = 11$, and so

$$\cos\theta = \frac{-3}{\sqrt{9} \times \sqrt{11}} = \frac{-1}{\sqrt{11}},$$

by which a unique value for θ in the range $0 \leqslant \theta \leqslant \pi$ is determined.

Example (ii). Prove that if two pairs of opposite edges of a tetrahedron are mutually perpendicular, then the third pair are also mutually perpendicular.

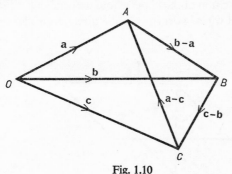

Fig. 1.10

In Fig. 1.10, O is any vertex and $\mathbf{a}, \mathbf{b}, \mathbf{c}$ are vectors $\overrightarrow{OA}$, $\overrightarrow{OB}$, $\overrightarrow{OC}$ forming the edges which meet at O. The remaining edges are represented by the vectors indicated. Suppose we are given that OA and OB are respectively perpendicular to BC and CA, and so need to prove that OC is perpendicular to AB. The given conditions are expressed vectorially as

$$\mathbf{a} \cdot (\mathbf{c} - \mathbf{b}) = 0, \qquad \mathbf{b} \cdot (\mathbf{a} - \mathbf{c}) = 0.$$

On adding these two equations we get (since $\mathbf{a} \cdot \mathbf{b} = \mathbf{b} \cdot \mathbf{a}$)

$$\mathbf{a} \cdot \mathbf{c} - \mathbf{b} \cdot \mathbf{c} = 0, \quad \text{i.e. } (\mathbf{a} - \mathbf{b}) \cdot \mathbf{c} = 0,$$

which proves the required result.

1.7 The Vector Equation of a Plane

Form 1. The equation of the plane which is parallel to two given (non-parallel) vectors $\mathbf{b}$ and $\mathbf{c}$, and which passes through the point $A(\mathbf{a})$. Let $P(\mathbf{r})$ be any point in the plane. Then the displacement in the plane from A to P can be expressed as the sum of two displacements, parallel to $\mathbf{b}$ and $\mathbf{c}$ respectively. Therefore,

$$\overrightarrow{AP} = \mathbf{r} - \mathbf{a} = s\mathbf{b} + t\mathbf{c},$$

for some real numbers s, t. It follows that the required equation is

$$\mathbf{r} = \mathbf{a} + s\mathbf{b} + t\mathbf{c} \qquad (-\infty < s < \infty, \quad -\infty < t < \infty.) \quad (1.12)$$

This should be compared with the vector equation of a straight line (p. 18).

(*Note:* The notation $A(\mathbf{a})$ means the point A whose position vector is **a** relative to the chosen origin.)

Form 2. The equation of the plane whose perpendicular distance from the origin is p and whose normal is in the direction of the *unit* vector $\hat{\mathbf{n}}$ (Fig. 1.11).

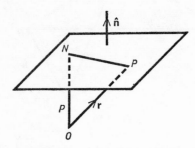

Fig. 1.11

In the Figure, $ON = p$ is drawn perpendicular to the given plane, and it is assumed that $\hat{\mathbf{n}}$ is directed in the same sense as $\overrightarrow{ON}$. Then, $\overrightarrow{ON} = p\hat{\mathbf{n}}$, and if $P(\mathbf{r})$ is any point in the plane, $\overrightarrow{NP}$ is perpendicular to $\hat{\mathbf{n}}$, and the required equation is

$$(\mathbf{r} - p\hat{\mathbf{n}}) . \hat{\mathbf{n}} = 0,$$

that is,

$$\mathbf{r} . \hat{\mathbf{n}} = p, \qquad (1.13)$$

since $\hat{\mathbf{n}} . \hat{\mathbf{n}} = 1$.

If $\hat{\mathbf{n}}$ is taken in the opposite direction to $\overrightarrow{ON}$, then (1.13) is to be replaced by $\mathbf{r} . \hat{\mathbf{n}} = -p$. More generally, if **n** denotes *any* vector normal to the plane, then, by (1.13) or the last result, we have

$$\mathbf{r} . \mathbf{n} = \mathbf{r} . \hat{\mathbf{n}}n = \pm np = q, \qquad (1.14)$$

where q is a constant scalar. Conversely, every equation of the form $\mathbf{r} . \mathbf{n} = q$ represents a plane, and $|q|/n$ is its perpendicular distance from the origin.

1.8 The Vector Product

A second important quantity which can be constructed from two vectors **a** and **b** is the *vector product* or *cross product*

$$\mathbf{a} \wedge \mathbf{b} = ab \sin \theta \, \hat{\mathbf{n}}, \qquad 0 \leqslant \theta \leqslant \pi \qquad (1.15)$$

(pronounced 'a cross b') where θ is the angle between the directions of **a** and **b**, and $\hat{\mathbf{n}}$ is a unit vector perpendicular to both **a** and **b** (Fig. 1.12).

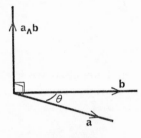

Fig. 1.12

The sense of direction of $\hat{\mathbf{n}}$ is determined according to the 'right hand rule'. Let **a** and **b** be drawn from a common initial point, and let a right handed corkscrew point in a direction normal to **a** and **b**, its handle being in the plane of **a** and **b**. Then, when the handle is rotated in the same sense as the rotation through θ which takes **a** into the direction **b**, the screw will move in the direction $\hat{\mathbf{n}}$.

Note that this product of two vectors is itself a vector, and also that vector multiplication of **a** and **b** is *not* commutative. For, according to the right hand rule, $\mathbf{b} \wedge \mathbf{a}$ is in the opposite direction to $\mathbf{a} \wedge \mathbf{b}$, and so by (1.15), we find

$$\mathbf{b} \wedge \mathbf{a} = -(\mathbf{a} \wedge \mathbf{b}). \qquad (1.16)$$

An alternative notation for the vector product of **a** and **b** is $\mathbf{a} \times \mathbf{b}$.

Example (i). The *moment* of a force **F** about a point O is defined to be the vector $\mathbf{M} = \mathbf{r} \wedge \mathbf{F}$, where **r** is the vector from O to any point P on the line of action of **F** (Fig. 1.13). We have $M = rF \sin \theta = pF$, where p is the perpendicular distance from O to the line of action of **F**. A rigid body free to rotate about the fixed point O, but initially at rest, would be caused to rotate about an axis in the direction of **M** by the application of the force **F** at the point P in the body. The magnitude $M = pF$ is the ordinary scalar moment of **F** about this axis. Clearly, this shows that **M** is independent of the point P on the line of action of **F**. Note that **M** defines a sense of direction of the rotation axis, and we say that **F** applied at P would tend to cause a *positive* rotation about an axis in the direction **M** (which is into the plane of the paper in Fig. 1.13).

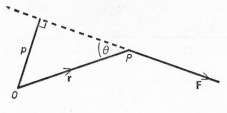

Fig. 1.13

Definition. A *positive* rotation about an axis in the direction of a vector **a** is one which would cause a right handed screw lying along the axis to move in the direction **a**.

Example (ii). The velocity of any point in a rigid body rotating about an axis **â** through a fixed point O. Suppose that **â** is drawn in the direction

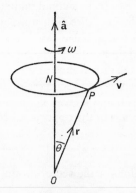

Fig. 1.14

such that the rotation is positive about **â**, and that the angular speed is ω. Then $\boldsymbol{\omega} = \omega\hat{\mathbf{a}}$ is called the *angular velocity vector*. By inspection of Fig. 1.14, where P is any point fixed in the body and PN is perpendicular to the vector **â**, we see that the velocity of P has magnitude $NP \cdot \omega$ and is in the direction of $\boldsymbol{\omega} \wedge \mathbf{r}$, where $\overrightarrow{OP} = \mathbf{r}$. But $NP \cdot \omega = OP \cdot \sin\theta \cdot \omega$

$= |\boldsymbol{\omega} \wedge \mathbf{r}|$. Combining these results, we find that the velocity of P is given in magnitude and direction by the vector

$$\mathbf{v} = \boldsymbol{\omega} \wedge \mathbf{r}. \tag{1.17}$$

If two vectors $\mathbf{a}$ and $\mathbf{b}$ are parallel, then $\sin\theta = 0$ in (1.15) and $\mathbf{a} \wedge \mathbf{b} = 0$. In particular, $\mathbf{a} \wedge \mathbf{a} = 0$ for any vector $\mathbf{a}$.

For the unit vectors $\mathbf{i}, \mathbf{j}$ and $\mathbf{k}$, it follows from (1.15) that

$$\mathbf{i} \wedge \mathbf{i} = \quad \mathbf{j} \wedge \mathbf{j} = \mathbf{k} \wedge \mathbf{k} = 0,$$
$$\mathbf{i} \wedge \mathbf{j} = \quad -\mathbf{j} \wedge \mathbf{i} = \mathbf{k},$$
$$\mathbf{j} \wedge \mathbf{k} = -\mathbf{k} \wedge \mathbf{j} = \mathbf{i},$$
$$\mathbf{k} \wedge \mathbf{i} = -\mathbf{i} \wedge \mathbf{k} = \mathbf{j}. \tag{1.18}$$

We next prove the distributive law

$$\mathbf{a} \wedge (\mathbf{b} + \mathbf{c}) = \mathbf{a} \wedge \mathbf{b} + \mathbf{a} \wedge \mathbf{c} \tag{1.19}$$

for any three vectors $\mathbf{a}, \mathbf{b}$ and $\mathbf{c}$. In Fig. (1.15), the triangle $P'Q'R'$ is the projection on a plane perpendicular to $\mathbf{a}$ of the triangle PQR whose sides are parallel to $\mathbf{b}, \mathbf{c}$ and $\mathbf{b} + \mathbf{c}$ as shown. We may suppose $|\mathbf{a}| = 1$. (Otherwise, except in the trivial case $\mathbf{a} = 0$, divide (1.19) by $|\mathbf{a}|$.)

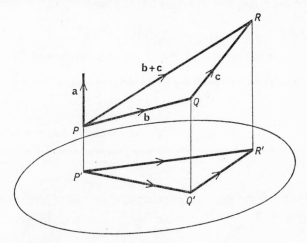

Fig. 1.15

Consider $\mathbf{a} \wedge \mathbf{b}$. This vector has magnitude $b \sin \theta$, where θ is the angle between $\overrightarrow{PQ}$ and $\mathbf{a}$, and so $|\mathbf{a} \wedge \mathbf{b}| = P'Q'$. The direction of $\mathbf{a} \wedge \mathbf{b}$ is at right angles to the plane of $\mathbf{a}$ and $\mathbf{b}$, and with the right hand rule taken into account it follows that $\mathbf{a} \wedge \mathbf{b}$ is the vector obtained by rotating $\overrightarrow{P'Q'}$

positively through 90° about the axis $\mathbf{a}$. Similarly, the vectors $\mathbf{a} \wedge \mathbf{c}$ and $\mathbf{a} \wedge (\mathbf{b}+\mathbf{c})$ are obtained respectively by rotating $\overrightarrow{Q'R'}$ and $\overrightarrow{P'R'}$ through the same angle about the same axis. Thus, the vectors $\mathbf{a} \wedge \mathbf{b}$, $\mathbf{a} \wedge \mathbf{c}$ and $\mathbf{a} \wedge (\mathbf{b}+\mathbf{c})$ are the sides $\overrightarrow{P''Q''}$, $\overrightarrow{Q''R''}$ and $\overrightarrow{P''R''}$ of the triangle obtained by projecting and rotating the triangle PQR as a whole, in the manner described. The relation (1.19) then follows immediately from the result

$$\overrightarrow{P''R''} = \overrightarrow{P''Q''} + \overrightarrow{Q''R''}.$$

Note that if $\mathbf{a}$, $\mathbf{b}$ and $\mathbf{c}$ are coplanar, then the points P', Q', R' lie in a straight line. The above method of proof remains valid, although in this special case the wording of the proof needs amendment.

By (1.16), we obtain from (1.19)

$$(\mathbf{b}+\mathbf{c}) \wedge \mathbf{a} = \mathbf{b} \wedge \mathbf{a} + \mathbf{c} \wedge \mathbf{a}, \tag{1.20}$$

which is another form of distributive law.

Repeated use of (1.19), (1.20) and the relations (1.18) enables us to express vector products in terms of rectangular components. Let $\mathbf{a} = a_1\mathbf{i}+a_2\mathbf{j}+a_3\mathbf{k}$, $\mathbf{b} = b_1\mathbf{i}+b_2\mathbf{j}+b_3\mathbf{k}$. Then

$$\mathbf{a} \wedge \mathbf{b} = (a_1\mathbf{i}+a_2\mathbf{j}+a_3\mathbf{k}) \wedge (b_1\mathbf{i}+b_2\mathbf{j}+b_3\mathbf{k})$$
$$= (a_2 b_3 - a_3 b_2)\mathbf{i} + (a_3 b_1 - a_1 b_3)\mathbf{j} + (a_1 b_2 - a_2 b_1)\mathbf{k}, \tag{1.21}$$

which can be expressed formally as the determinant

$$\mathbf{a} \wedge \mathbf{b} = \begin{vmatrix} \mathbf{i} & \mathbf{j} & \mathbf{k} \\ a_1 & a_2 & a_3 \\ b_1 & b_2 & b_3 \end{vmatrix}. \tag{1.22}$$

Example (i). Use the vector product to find a unit vector perpendicular to the two vectors $\mathbf{a} = 2\mathbf{i}+\mathbf{j}-\mathbf{k}$, $\mathbf{b} = \mathbf{i}+\mathbf{j}+\mathbf{k}$.

We have

$$\mathbf{a} \wedge \mathbf{b} = \begin{vmatrix} \mathbf{i} & \mathbf{j} & \mathbf{k} \\ 2 & 1 & -1 \\ 1 & 1 & 1 \end{vmatrix} = 2\mathbf{i}-3\mathbf{j}+\mathbf{k},$$

which is a vector perpendicular to both $\mathbf{a}$ and $\mathbf{b}$. But

$$|\mathbf{a} \wedge \mathbf{b}| = \sqrt{(4+9+1)} = \sqrt{14}.$$

Therefore the two vectors

$$\pm \frac{1}{\sqrt{14}} \mathbf{a} \wedge \mathbf{b} = \pm \frac{1}{\sqrt{14}} (2\mathbf{i} - 3\mathbf{j} + \mathbf{k})$$

are each unit vectors orthogonal to both **a** and **b**. They are in opposite directions.

Example (ii). Find the area of the triangle with vertices at the points $A(\mathbf{a})$, $B(\mathbf{b})$, $C(\mathbf{c})$.

The area of the triangle ABC is

$$\begin{aligned}
\tfrac{1}{2}AB \cdot AC \sin BAC &= \tfrac{1}{2}|\overrightarrow{AB} \wedge \overrightarrow{AC}| \\
&= \tfrac{1}{2}|(\mathbf{b} - \mathbf{a}) \wedge (\mathbf{c} - \mathbf{a})| \\
&= \tfrac{1}{2}|\mathbf{b} \wedge \mathbf{c} + \mathbf{c} \wedge \mathbf{a} + \mathbf{a} \wedge \mathbf{b}|,
\end{aligned}$$

using (1.16), since $\mathbf{a} \wedge \mathbf{a} = 0$.

The vector

$$\mathbf{d} = \tfrac{1}{2}(\mathbf{b} \wedge \mathbf{c} + \mathbf{c} \wedge \mathbf{a} + \mathbf{a} \wedge \mathbf{b})$$

is normal to the plane of the triangle, since it is in the direction of $\overrightarrow{AB} \wedge \overrightarrow{AC}$. It is called the *vector area* of the triangle ABC. The direction of **d** is such that a point describing the perimeter would make a positive rotation about an axis **d**, through any interior point of the triangle, if the vertices are met in the order A, B, C.

Division by a vector is not defined. Furthermore, the cancellation of factors in products of vectors is not permissible. For example, the equation

$$\mathbf{a} \wedge \mathbf{b} = \mathbf{a} \wedge \mathbf{c} \qquad (1.23)$$

does not imply that $\mathbf{b} = \mathbf{c}$, but merely that $\mathbf{a} \wedge (\mathbf{b} - \mathbf{c}) = 0$, from which it follows that $\mathbf{b} - \mathbf{c}$ is parallel to **a**, i.e. $\mathbf{b} = \mathbf{c} + k\mathbf{a}$ for some real number k. This is all that can be deduced about **b** and **c** from (1.23). Similarly, the relation

$$\mathbf{a} \cdot \mathbf{b} = \mathbf{a} \cdot \mathbf{c}$$

implies only that $\mathbf{b} - \mathbf{c}$ is perpendicular to **a**.

1.9 The Scalar Triple Product

Products involving three vectors occur frequently in practice. If $\mathbf{a}, \mathbf{b}$ and $\mathbf{c}$ are any three vectors, then we can form the products

$$(\mathbf{a} \cdot \mathbf{b})\mathbf{c}, \quad \mathbf{a} \cdot (\mathbf{b} \wedge \mathbf{c}), \quad \mathbf{a} \wedge (\mathbf{b} \wedge \mathbf{c}).$$

By enumeration of all possibilities it is easy to see that only these forms, or trivial variants of them, can be constructed as products of three vectors. There is no meaning to expressions such as $(\mathbf{a}.\mathbf{b}).\mathbf{c}$ and $(\mathbf{a}.\mathbf{b}) \wedge \mathbf{c}$, because $\mathbf{a}.\mathbf{b}$ is a scalar and so its scalar and vector products with $\mathbf{c}$ are not defined.

The first of the three stated products is simply a vector in the direction of $\pm\mathbf{c}$ with magnitude $|\mathbf{a}.\mathbf{b}|\,|\mathbf{c}|$ and needs no further discussion. The second expression, $\mathbf{a}.(\mathbf{b} \wedge \mathbf{c})$, is called the *scalar triple product* of $\mathbf{a}, \mathbf{b}$ and $\mathbf{c}$. Let $\overrightarrow{OA} = \mathbf{a}, \overrightarrow{OB} = \mathbf{b}, \overrightarrow{OC} = \mathbf{c}$, and construct the parallelepiped with concurrent edges OA, OB, OC and volume V (Fig. 1.16). The base

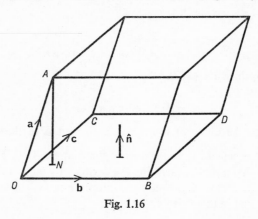

Fig. 1.16

parallelogram $OBDC$ has area $|\mathbf{b} \wedge \mathbf{c}|$, and the unit vector $\hat{\mathbf{n}}$ in the direction of $\mathbf{b} \wedge \mathbf{c}$ is normal to the base. Therefore, if AN is the perpendicular from A to the base, then since $\mathbf{b} \wedge \mathbf{c} = |\mathbf{b} \wedge \mathbf{c}|\hat{\mathbf{n}}$,

$$\mathbf{a}.(\mathbf{b} \wedge \mathbf{c}) = \mathbf{a}.\hat{\mathbf{n}}|\mathbf{b} \wedge \mathbf{c}| = \pm AN|\mathbf{b} \wedge \mathbf{c}| = \pm V,$$

where V is the volume of the parallelepiped. In the case shown in the Figure, $\mathbf{a}$ makes an acute angle with $\mathbf{b} \wedge \mathbf{c}$ and so $\mathbf{a}.\hat{\mathbf{n}}$ is positive, making the $(+)$ sign necessary.

As a generalization of a right handed set of orthogonal vectors, we say non-coplanar vectors $\mathbf{a}, \mathbf{b}, \mathbf{c}$, in that order, form a *right handed system* when $\mathbf{a}$ makes an acute angle with $\mathbf{b} \wedge \mathbf{c}$. In this case, the scalar triple product $\mathbf{a}.(\mathbf{b} \wedge \mathbf{c})$ is positive.

From Fig. 1.16, it follows that the three vectors in a scalar triple product may be permuted cyclically without changing its value. Since, also, the order of factors in a scalar product is immaterial, we have that

$$\mathbf{a}.(\mathbf{b} \wedge \mathbf{c}) = \mathbf{b}.(\mathbf{c} \wedge \mathbf{a}) = \mathbf{c}.(\mathbf{a} \wedge \mathbf{b}) = (\mathbf{b} \wedge \mathbf{c}).\mathbf{a} = (\mathbf{c} \wedge \mathbf{a}).\mathbf{b} = (\mathbf{a} \wedge \mathbf{b}).\mathbf{c}.$$
$$(1.24)$$

This result may be summarized by saying that the six scalar triple products which can be formed by writing $\mathbf{a}, \mathbf{b}, \mathbf{c}$ in that or cyclically similar order, irrespective of the positions of the dot and the cross, are all equal. The other six, with opposite cyclic order, are also equal to one another and have minus the value of those in (1.24). This follows because each is equal to $\mathbf{a} \cdot (\mathbf{c} \wedge \mathbf{b}) = -\mathbf{a} \cdot (\mathbf{b} \wedge \mathbf{c})$, by (1.16).

Note that if $\mathbf{a}, \mathbf{b}, \mathbf{c}$ are coplanar, then $\mathbf{a} \cdot (\mathbf{b} \wedge \mathbf{c}) = 0$, since $V = 0$. The vanishing of the scalar triple product is a necessary and sufficient condition for coplanarity. A particular case of this arises when any two of the three vectors are equal or parallel.

In terms of rectangular components, in the usual notation we have

$$\mathbf{a} \cdot (\mathbf{b} \wedge \mathbf{c}) = (a_1 \mathbf{i} + a_2 \mathbf{j} + a_3 \mathbf{k}) \cdot \{(b_2 c_3 - b_3 c_2)\mathbf{i}$$
$$+ (b_3 c_1 - b_1 c_3)\mathbf{j} + (b_1 c_2 - b_2 c_1)\mathbf{k}\}$$
$$= a_1(b_2 c_3 - b_3 c_2) + a_2(b_3 c_1 - b_1 c_3) + a_3(b_1 c_2 - b_2 c_1)$$
$$= \begin{vmatrix} a_1 & a_2 & a_3 \\ b_1 & b_2 & b_3 \\ c_1 & c_2 & c_3 \end{vmatrix}. \tag{1.25}$$

Example (i). Show that the four points A, B, C, D with rectangular cartesian coordinates $(4, 5, 1)$, $(0, -1, -1)$, $(3, 9, 4)$, $(-4, 4, 4)$, respectively, are coplanar (i.e. lie in a plane).

A necessary and sufficient condition for the given points to be coplanar is that the vectors $\overrightarrow{AB}, \overrightarrow{AC}$ and $\overrightarrow{AD}$ be coplanar.

$$\overrightarrow{AB} = (-\mathbf{j} - \mathbf{k}) - (4\mathbf{i} + 5\mathbf{j} + \mathbf{k}) = -4\mathbf{i} - 6\mathbf{j} - 2\mathbf{k}.$$

Similarly we find

$$\overrightarrow{AC} = -\mathbf{i} + 4\mathbf{j} + 3\mathbf{k}, \qquad \overrightarrow{AD} = -8\mathbf{i} - \mathbf{j} + 3\mathbf{k}.$$

Thus,

$$\overrightarrow{AB} \cdot (\overrightarrow{AC} \wedge \overrightarrow{AD}) = \begin{vmatrix} -4 & -6 & -2 \\ -1 & 4 & 3 \\ -8 & -1 & 3 \end{vmatrix}$$
$$= -4(15) + 6(21) - 2(33) = 0,$$

and so the given points are coplanar.

Example (ii). Let $\mathbf{r} = l\mathbf{a} + m\mathbf{b} + n\mathbf{c}$, where $\mathbf{r}$ is any given vector and $\mathbf{a}, \mathbf{b}, \mathbf{c}$ are given non-coplanar vectors (cf. p. 15). Determine the scalars l, m, n.

To eliminate m and n from the given relation, take the scalar product of each side with $\mathbf{b} \wedge \mathbf{c}$. Since $\mathbf{b} . (\mathbf{b} \wedge \mathbf{c}) = \mathbf{c} . (\mathbf{b} \wedge \mathbf{c}) = 0$, we get

$$\mathbf{r} . (\mathbf{b} \wedge \mathbf{c}) = l\mathbf{a} . (\mathbf{b} \wedge \mathbf{c}). \tag{1.26}$$

Similarly, by scalar multiplication of the given relation by $\mathbf{c} \wedge \mathbf{a}$ and $\mathbf{a} \wedge \mathbf{b}$, in turn, we can eliminate respectively n, l and l, m, and obtain two further relations similar to (1.26). Using the cyclic property of scalar triple products, we thus find

$$l = \frac{\mathbf{r} . (\mathbf{b} \wedge \mathbf{c})}{\mathbf{a} . (\mathbf{b} \wedge \mathbf{c})}, \qquad m = \frac{\mathbf{r} . (\mathbf{c} \wedge \mathbf{a})}{\mathbf{a} . (\mathbf{b} \wedge \mathbf{c})}, \qquad n = \frac{\mathbf{r} . (\mathbf{a} \wedge \mathbf{b})}{\mathbf{a} . (\mathbf{b} \wedge \mathbf{c})},$$

where the denominators do not vanish because $\mathbf{a}, \mathbf{b}$ and $\mathbf{c}$ are given to be non-coplanar.

1.10   The Vector Triple Product

We consider now the *vector triple product*

$$\mathbf{a} \wedge (\mathbf{b} \wedge \mathbf{c}). \tag{1.27}$$

Let the three vectors be given a common initial point. Since the vector $\mathbf{n} = \mathbf{b} \wedge \mathbf{c}$ is perpendicular to the plane containing $\mathbf{b}$ and $\mathbf{c}$, and $\mathbf{a} \wedge \mathbf{n}$ is perpendicular to $\mathbf{n}$, it follows that the vector (1.27) is in the plane of $\mathbf{b}$ and $\mathbf{c}$, and therefore

$$\mathbf{a} \wedge (\mathbf{b} \wedge \mathbf{c}) = l\mathbf{b} + m\mathbf{c},$$

for some scalars l and m. To find l and m in terms of $\mathbf{a}, \mathbf{b}$ and $\mathbf{c}$, introduce rectangular coordinate axes so that Oz is along $\mathbf{c}$, and the yz plane is the plane of $\mathbf{b}$ and $\mathbf{c}$. Then, in the usual notation, we have the following simplified component forms

$$\mathbf{a} = a_1 \mathbf{i} + a_2 \mathbf{j} + a_3 \mathbf{k}, \quad \mathbf{b} = b_2 \mathbf{j} + b_3 \mathbf{k}, \quad \mathbf{c} = c_3 \mathbf{k}.$$

Direct calculation shows that

$$\mathbf{b} \wedge \mathbf{c} = b_2 c_3 \mathbf{i},$$

and

$$\begin{aligned}
\mathbf{a} \wedge (\mathbf{b} \wedge \mathbf{c}) &= -a_2 b_2 c_3 \mathbf{k} + a_3 b_2 c_3 \mathbf{j} \\
&= a_3 c_3 (b_2 \mathbf{j} + b_3 \mathbf{k}) - (a_2 b_2 + a_3 b_3) c_3 \mathbf{k} \\
&= (\mathbf{a} . \mathbf{c}) \mathbf{b} - (\mathbf{a} . \mathbf{b}) \mathbf{c}. \tag{1.28}
\end{aligned}$$

Similarly, we can obtain an expression for $(\mathbf{a} \wedge \mathbf{b}) \wedge \mathbf{c}$. More simply, we have

$$
\begin{aligned}
(\mathbf{a} \wedge \mathbf{b}) \wedge \mathbf{c} &= -\mathbf{c} \wedge (\mathbf{a} \wedge \mathbf{b}) \\
&= \mathbf{c} \wedge (\mathbf{b} \wedge \mathbf{a}) \\
&= (\mathbf{a} . \mathbf{c})\mathbf{b} - (\mathbf{b} . \mathbf{c})\mathbf{a} \qquad \text{(by (1.28))}
\end{aligned}
\qquad (1.29)
$$

Note that there is no simple relation between the triple products $\mathbf{a} \wedge (\mathbf{b} \wedge \mathbf{c})$ and $(\mathbf{a} \wedge \mathbf{b}) \wedge \mathbf{c}$. The first is a vector coplanar with $\mathbf{b}$ and $\mathbf{c}$, while the second is coplanar with $\mathbf{a}$ and $\mathbf{b}$. However, the same rule may be used to remember both formulae (1.28) and (1.29). Write down the middle vector and multiply it by the scalar product of the other pair. Then subtract the other bracketed vector multiplied by the scalar product of the remaining pair.

Example. Express $(\mathbf{a} \wedge \mathbf{b}) . (\mathbf{c} \wedge \mathbf{d})$ entirely in terms of scalar products.

Write $\mathbf{c} \wedge \mathbf{d} = \mathbf{e}$. Then

$$
\begin{aligned}
(\mathbf{a} \wedge \mathbf{b}) . (\mathbf{c} \wedge \mathbf{d}) &= (\mathbf{a} \wedge \mathbf{b}) . \mathbf{e} \\
&= \mathbf{a} . (\mathbf{b} \wedge \mathbf{e}) \qquad \text{(interchanging dot and cross)} \\
&= \mathbf{a} . \{\mathbf{b} \wedge (\mathbf{c} \wedge \mathbf{d})\} \\
&= \mathbf{a} . \{(\mathbf{b} . \mathbf{d})\mathbf{c} - (\mathbf{b} . \mathbf{c})\mathbf{d}\} \\
&= (\mathbf{a} . \mathbf{c})(\mathbf{b} . \mathbf{d}) - (\mathbf{a} . \mathbf{d})(\mathbf{b} . \mathbf{c}).
\end{aligned}
$$

EXERCISES

1. If $\mathbf{a} = \mathbf{i} - \mathbf{j}$, $\mathbf{b} = 2\mathbf{i} + 3\mathbf{j} - \mathbf{k}$, $\mathbf{c} = \mathbf{j} + \mathbf{k}$, find (i) $\mathbf{a} + \mathbf{b}$, (ii) $\mathbf{a} - 2\mathbf{b} + \mathbf{c}$, (iii) $\mathbf{c} - 3(\mathbf{a} + \mathbf{b})$. What is the terminal point of the vector $\mathbf{a} - 2\mathbf{b} + \mathbf{c}$ if its initial point is the point $(1, 0, 0)$?

2. Find a unit vector parallel to the sum of the vectors $3\mathbf{i} + 3\mathbf{j} + \mathbf{k}$, $-2\mathbf{i} + \mathbf{j} - 2\mathbf{k}$.

3. Let $\mathbf{a} = 2\mathbf{i} + \mathbf{j} - 3\mathbf{k}$, $\mathbf{b} = -\mathbf{i} + \mathbf{j} + 2\mathbf{k}$, $\mathbf{c} = 4\mathbf{i} + 3\mathbf{k}$. Find (i) the magnitudes, (ii) the direction cosines, of $\mathbf{a} - \mathbf{b}$, $\mathbf{b} - \mathbf{a}$, $\mathbf{a} + \mathbf{b} + 2\mathbf{c}$.

4. Prove that the points $(1, 1, 2)$, $(3, 2, 4)$, $(7, 4, 8)$ are collinear.

5. Show that the diagonals of a parallelogram bisect each other.

6. If n vectors $\mathbf{a}_1, \mathbf{a}_2, \ldots, \mathbf{a}_n$ are such that there are real numbers $c_1, c_2, \ldots, c_n$, not all zero, for which

$$
c_1 \mathbf{a}_1 + c_2 \mathbf{a}_2 + \ldots + c_n \mathbf{a}_n = 0,
$$

then the vectors are said to be *linearly dependent*. In this case, each vector $\mathbf{a}_i$ $(i = 1, 2, \ldots, n)$, such that $c_i \neq 0$, is said to be linearly dependent on the other $\mathbf{a}$'s, which means that it may be expressed in the form

$$
\mathbf{a}_i = d_1 \mathbf{a}_1 + d_2 \mathbf{a}_2 + \ldots + d_{i-1} \mathbf{a}_{i-1} + d_{i+1} \mathbf{a}_{i+1} + \ldots + d_n \mathbf{a}_n,
$$

where the d's are real numbers. (Take $d_1 = -c_1/c_i$, $d_2 = -c_2/c_i$, etc.) When n vectors are not linearly dependent, they are *linearly independent*.

Prove that

(i) the three vectors $2\mathbf{i}+\mathbf{j}+\mathbf{k}$, $\mathbf{i}-2\mathbf{j}+\mathbf{k}$, $\mathbf{i}+8\mathbf{j}-\mathbf{k}$,

(ii) any four vectors,

are linearly dependent.

Prove also that when two vectors are linearly dependent they are both parallel to the same line, and when three vectors are linearly dependent they are all parallel to a plane.

7.   Find the angle between the vectors $\mathbf{i}+\mathbf{j}+\mathbf{k}$ and $2\mathbf{i}-\mathbf{j}-2\mathbf{k}$.

8.   A force of magnitude 6 units in the direction $\overrightarrow{AB}$ acts along the line joining the points $A(2,1,0)$ and $B(3,-1,2)$. Find its moment about (i) the origin, (ii) the point $(1,1,-2)$.

9.   A rigid body rotates about an axis in the direction of the vector $2\mathbf{i}+\mathbf{j}+2\mathbf{k}$, through the fixed point $(2,-1,3)$. If the angular speed is 12 radians sec^{-1}, show that the particle of the body instantaneously at the point $(-3,-2,3)$ has the velocity $4\sqrt{(113)}$ units in the direction of the vector $2\mathbf{i}-10\mathbf{j}+3\mathbf{k}$.

10.   For the vectors $\mathbf{a},\mathbf{b},\mathbf{c}$ in question 3, find

$$\mathbf{a}.(\mathbf{b}\wedge\mathbf{c}), \quad \mathbf{a}\wedge(\mathbf{b}\wedge\mathbf{c}), \quad (\mathbf{a}\wedge\mathbf{b})\wedge\mathbf{c}$$

11.   Use the vector product to determine a unit vector orthogonal to each of the vectors $\mathbf{a} = \mathbf{i}-\mathbf{j}+\mathbf{k}$, $\mathbf{b} = 2\mathbf{i}+2\mathbf{j}+\mathbf{k}$. Hence obtain in the form (1.14) the equation of the plane which is parallel to the two vectors $\mathbf{a}$ and $\mathbf{b}$ and passes through the point $(1,0,2)$. State its perpendicular distance from the origin.

12.   Prove that if the straight lines $\mathbf{r} = \mathbf{a}+s(\mathbf{b}+\mathbf{c})$, $\mathbf{r} = \mathbf{b}+t(\mathbf{c}-\mathbf{a})$ $(-\infty < s < \infty, -\infty < t < \infty)$ intersect, then the vectors $\mathbf{a},\mathbf{b},\mathbf{c}$ are coplanar.

13.   Find the equation of the plane containing the parallel lines

$$\mathbf{r} = \mathbf{a}+s\mathbf{b}, \quad \mathbf{r} = \mathbf{a}'+t\mathbf{b} \quad (-\infty < s < \infty, \; -\infty < t < \infty).$$

14.   Show that the length of the common perpendicular to the skew (non-parallel) lines $\mathbf{r} = \mathbf{a}+s\mathbf{b}, \mathbf{r} = \mathbf{a}'+t\mathbf{b}'$ $(-\infty < s < \infty, -\infty < t < \infty)$ is

$$\pm\frac{(\mathbf{b}\wedge\mathbf{b}').(\mathbf{a}-\mathbf{a}')}{|\mathbf{b}\wedge\mathbf{b}'|}$$

where the sign is chosen so as to make the expression positive.

15.   Prove that

$(\mathbf{b}\wedge\mathbf{c})\wedge(\mathbf{a}\wedge\mathbf{d})+(\mathbf{c}\wedge\mathbf{a})\wedge(\mathbf{b}\wedge\mathbf{d})+(\mathbf{a}\wedge\mathbf{b})\wedge(\mathbf{c}\wedge\mathbf{d}) = -2\{\mathbf{a}.(\mathbf{b}\wedge\mathbf{c})\}\mathbf{d}$.

16.   State which of the following relations are true and which are false, $\mathbf{a}$, $\mathbf{b}$, $\mathbf{c}$ being general vectors:

(i) $\mathbf{a}.\mathbf{a} = 0$,

(ii) $\mathbf{a}.\mathbf{b} = \mathbf{b}.\mathbf{a}$,

(iii) $\mathbf{a}\wedge\mathbf{b} = \mathbf{b}\wedge\mathbf{a}$,

(iv) $\mathbf{a}\wedge\mathbf{b} = -\mathbf{b}\wedge\mathbf{a}$,

(v) $\mathbf{i}\wedge\mathbf{i} = 1$,

(vi) $\mathbf{i}.\mathbf{i} = 0$,

(vii) $\mathbf{a}.(\mathbf{a}\wedge\mathbf{b}) = 0$,

(viii) $\mathbf{i}.(\mathbf{j}\wedge\mathbf{k}) = 1$,

(ix) $\mathbf{a}.(\mathbf{b}\wedge\mathbf{c}) = (\mathbf{a}\wedge\mathbf{b}).\mathbf{c}$,

(x) $\mathbf{a}.(\mathbf{b}\wedge\mathbf{c}) = \mathbf{c}.(\mathbf{a}\wedge\mathbf{b})$
$= \mathbf{b}.(\mathbf{c}\wedge\mathbf{a})$,

(xi) $\mathbf{a}\wedge(\mathbf{b}\wedge\mathbf{c}) = (\mathbf{a}\wedge\mathbf{b})\wedge\mathbf{c}$,

(xii) $\mathbf{a}\wedge(\mathbf{b}\wedge\mathbf{c}) = (\mathbf{a}.\mathbf{c})\mathbf{b}-(\mathbf{a}.\mathbf{b})\mathbf{c}$,

(xiii) $\mathbf{a}\wedge(\mathbf{a}\wedge\mathbf{b}) = 0$,

(xiv) $\mathbf{i}\wedge(\mathbf{j}\wedge\mathbf{k}) = 0$,

(xv) $\mathbf{a}\wedge(\mathbf{b}\wedge\mathbf{b}) = 0$,

(xvi) $(\mathbf{a}\wedge\mathbf{b})\wedge(\mathbf{a}\wedge\mathbf{b}) = 0$.

CHAPTER 2

Differentiation and Integration of Vectors

2.1 Vector Functions of a Scalar Variable

The position vector $\mathbf{r}$ of a moving particle P relative to the origin O is a function of the time t, and we denote this by writing $\mathbf{r} = \mathbf{r}(t)$. Equally well, we can think of $\mathbf{r}$ as a function of the arc distance s travelled by P along its path in space, where s is measured from a chosen point on the path, and so we also have $\mathbf{r} = \mathbf{r}(s)$. The velocity vector of P is also a function of t or of s. These are all examples of a vector function of a scalar variable.

Let $\mathbf{a}(u)$ be a vector function of a scalar variable u. We say that $\mathbf{a}(u)$ is *continuous* at u if

$$\lim_{\Delta u \to 0} \{\mathbf{a}(u + \Delta u) - \mathbf{a}(u)\} = 0. \tag{2.1}$$

This means that the change in the vector $\mathbf{a}$ corresponding to a positive or negative increment Δu in u can be made as small as we please provided we choose $|\Delta u|$ sufficiently small. In what follows we shall normally assume that we are dealing with continuous vector functions.

2.2 Derivatives of Vectors

Let $\Delta \mathbf{a}$ denote the change in $\mathbf{a}(u)$ corresponding to the increment Δu in u

$$\Delta \mathbf{a} = \mathbf{a}(u + \Delta u) - \mathbf{a}(u). \tag{2.2}$$

In Fig. 2.1, $\overrightarrow{PP'} = \Delta \mathbf{a}$. If $\overrightarrow{PP'}/\Delta u$ tends to a definite limit as Δu tends to zero, then this limit is called the *derivative* of $\mathbf{a}$ with respect to u. Therefore, the derivative is itself a vector, written

$$\frac{d\mathbf{a}}{du} = \lim_{\Delta u \to 0} \frac{\mathbf{a}(u + \Delta u) - \mathbf{a}(u)}{\Delta u}, \tag{2.3}$$

C

provided the limit exists. By (2.1), a necessary condition, though not a sufficient one, for the derivative to exist is that $\mathbf{a}(u)$ be continuous at u. From the definition, it is clear that the direction of the derivative vector is that of the tangent at P to the curve $\mathbf{a}(u)$, in the sense in which u is

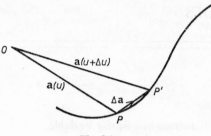

Fig. 2.1

increasing. For example, the velocity vector of a particle whose position vector at time t is $\mathbf{r}(t)$ is

$$\mathbf{v}(t) = \frac{d\mathbf{r}}{dt},$$

which at each instant is in the direction of the tangent to the path of the particle and has magnitude equal to the speed. Since $\mathbf{v}$ is itself a function of t, we can differentiate again and obtain the *acceleration vector*

$$\frac{d\mathbf{v}}{dt} = \frac{d^2\mathbf{r}}{dt^2}.$$

The rectangular components of a vector $\mathbf{a}(u)$ will themselves be functions of u,

$$\mathbf{a}(u) = a_1(u)\mathbf{i} + a_2(u)\mathbf{j} + a_3(u)\mathbf{k}.$$

By (2.2),

$$\Delta \mathbf{a} = \{a_1(u + \Delta u) - a_1(u)\}\mathbf{i} + \{a_2(u + \Delta u) - a_2(u)\}\mathbf{j} + \{a_3(u + \Delta u) - a_3(u)\}\mathbf{k},$$

and on dividing by Δu and taking the limit as $\Delta u \to 0$ we get

$$\frac{d\mathbf{a}}{du} = \frac{da_1}{du}\mathbf{i} + \frac{da_2}{du}\mathbf{j} + \frac{da_3}{du}\mathbf{k}. \tag{2.4}$$

(Here we have assumed that $\mathbf{i}$, $\mathbf{j}$ and $\mathbf{k}$ have fixed directions for all u.)

Example. A particle P moves along a curve so that at time t its position is given by $x = a\cos t$, $y = a\sin t$, $z = bt$, where a and b are positive constants. Describe the motion, and calculate the velocity and acceleration vectors at time t.

The equation of the curve satisfies $x^2 + y^2 = a^2$, and so P moves on the surface of a cylinder of radius a with z axis as axis (Fig. 2.2). From

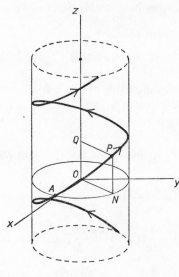

Fig. 2.2

the relations $x = a\cos t$, $y = a\sin t$ we see also that the projection of the path on the xy plane is a circle described with uniform speed, since t is equal to the polar angle AON. Because z increases uniformly with t, it follows that the motion is along a helix described with uniform speed.

With $\mathbf{r}$ denoting $\overrightarrow{OP}$, the velocity vector is

$$\mathbf{v} = \frac{d\mathbf{r}}{dt} = \frac{d}{dt}(a\cos t)\mathbf{i} + \frac{d}{dt}(a\sin t)\mathbf{j} + \frac{d}{dt}(bt)\mathbf{k},$$

$$= -a\sin t\,\mathbf{i} + a\cos t\,\mathbf{j} + b\mathbf{k}. \tag{2.5}$$

Note that

$$v^2 = a^2(\sin^2 t + \cos^2 t) + b^2$$
$$= a^2 + b^2$$

which confirms analytically that the speed is constant.

The acceleration vector is

$$\mathbf{f} = \frac{d\mathbf{v}}{dt} = -a\cos t\,\mathbf{i} - a\sin t\,\mathbf{j}. \tag{2.6}$$

We see that $|\mathbf{f}| = a$, and that

$$\mathbf{f} = -\mathbf{r} + z\mathbf{k}.$$

Thus, if Q is the point on the z axis such that PQ is perpendicular to Oz, then since $\overrightarrow{OQ} = z\mathbf{k}$, we have simply that $\mathbf{f} = \overrightarrow{PO} + \overrightarrow{OQ} = \overrightarrow{PQ}$.

2.3   Formal Rules of Differentiation

The following rules are easily verified. It is assumed that all vectors and scalars are functions of u and that derivatives exist and are continuous where necessary.

(1) $\dfrac{d\mathbf{c}}{du} = 0$,   if $\mathbf{c} =$ constant vector,

(2) $\dfrac{d}{du}(\mathbf{a} + \mathbf{b}) = \dfrac{d\mathbf{a}}{du} + \dfrac{d\mathbf{b}}{du}$,

(3) $\dfrac{d}{dw}\mathbf{a}(u) = \dfrac{du}{dw}\dfrac{d\mathbf{a}}{du}$,   if $u = u(w)$,

(4) $\dfrac{d}{du}(m\mathbf{a}) = m\dfrac{d\mathbf{a}}{du} + \dfrac{dm}{du}\mathbf{a}$,

(5) $\dfrac{d}{du}(\mathbf{a} \cdot \mathbf{b}) = \mathbf{a} \cdot \dfrac{d\mathbf{b}}{du} + \dfrac{d\mathbf{a}}{du} \cdot \mathbf{b}$,

(6) $\dfrac{d}{du}(\mathbf{a} \wedge \mathbf{b}) = \mathbf{a} \wedge \dfrac{d\mathbf{b}}{du} + \dfrac{d\mathbf{a}}{du} \wedge \mathbf{b}$,

where in (6) the order $\mathbf{a}$ before $\mathbf{b}$ must be retained. For example, to prove (5), let $\Delta\mathbf{a}$ and $\Delta\mathbf{b}$ be increments in $\mathbf{a}$ and $\mathbf{b}$ corresponding to an increment Δu in u. Then

$$\frac{d}{du}(\mathbf{a} \cdot \mathbf{b}) = \lim_{\Delta u \to 0} \frac{(\mathbf{a} + \Delta\mathbf{a}) \cdot (\mathbf{b} + \Delta\mathbf{b}) - \mathbf{a} \cdot \mathbf{b}}{\Delta u}$$

$$= \lim_{\Delta u \to 0} \left(\mathbf{a} \cdot \frac{\Delta\mathbf{b}}{\Delta u} + \frac{\Delta\mathbf{a}}{\Delta u} \cdot \mathbf{b} + \frac{\Delta\mathbf{a}}{\Delta u} \cdot \Delta\mathbf{b} \right)$$

$$= \mathbf{a} \cdot \frac{d\mathbf{b}}{du} + \frac{d\mathbf{a}}{du} \cdot \mathbf{b},$$

because the third term in parentheses tends to zero with $\Delta\mathbf{b}$, as $\Delta u \to 0$.

Example (i). If $\mathbf{a}(t)$ has constant magnitude, show that $d\mathbf{a}/dt$ is perpendicular to $\mathbf{a}$.

We have

$$\frac{d}{dt}(a^2) = 0 = \frac{d}{dt}(\mathbf{a}.\mathbf{a}) = \mathbf{a}.\frac{d\mathbf{a}}{dt} + \frac{d\mathbf{a}}{dt}.\mathbf{a} = 2\mathbf{a}.\frac{d\mathbf{a}}{dt}$$

Therefore $d\mathbf{a}/dt$ is perpendicular to $\mathbf{a}$.

Example (ii). In Newtonian mechanics, a particle whose mass is m and velocity $\mathbf{v}$ moves according to the law

$$\frac{d}{dt}(m\mathbf{v}) = \mathbf{F} \tag{2.7}$$

where $\mathbf{F}$ is the resultant applied force. ($m\mathbf{v}$ is the *momentum vector*.) Show that if m is constant and $\mathbf{F}$ is always perpendicular to $\mathbf{v}$, then the speed of the particle is constant.

We have that

$$\mathbf{v}.\frac{d}{dt}(m\mathbf{v}) = \mathbf{v}.\mathbf{F} = 0 \quad \text{(given)}$$

and so, since m is constant, $\mathbf{v}.d\mathbf{v}/dt = 0$. By the method of the last example, this gives

$$\frac{d}{dt}(v^2) = 0,$$

whence the speed v is constant.

A corresponding result holds even if the mass is a function of speed, as in the theory of special relativity where $m = m_0/\sqrt{(1-v^2/c^2)}$, m_0 and c being constants. To deal with this case, multiply both sides of (2.7) by $m\mathbf{v}$, and then show that m^2v^2 is constant.

Example (iii). The *angular momentum vector* of a particle about a fixed point O is (in the notation of the last example) the vector

$$\mathbf{h} = \mathbf{r} \wedge m\mathbf{v} \tag{2.8}$$

where $\mathbf{r}$ is the position vector of the particle with respect to O. Prove that if the moment of the force $\mathbf{F}$ about O is zero, then $\mathbf{h}$ is constant.

Differentiating (2.8) with respect to t, we get

$$\frac{d\mathbf{h}}{dt} = \frac{d}{dt}(\mathbf{r} \wedge m\mathbf{v})$$

$$= \frac{d\mathbf{r}}{dt} \wedge m\mathbf{v} + \mathbf{r} \wedge \frac{d}{dt}(m\mathbf{v})$$

$$= \mathbf{r} \wedge \frac{d}{dt}(m\mathbf{v})$$

$$= \mathbf{r} \wedge \mathbf{F} \tag{2.9}$$

where we have used $d\mathbf{r}/dt = \mathbf{v}$. Thus, given $\mathbf{r} \wedge \mathbf{F} = 0$, it follows that $\mathbf{h}$ is constant.

More generally, suppose that a system of n mass particles with masses $m_i(i = 1, 2, \ldots, n)$, and position vectors $\mathbf{r}_i$ relative to a fixed point O, are subject to forces, the resultant force on the ith particle being $\mathbf{F}_i$. Then the total angular momentum of the system about O is the vector sum

$$\mathbf{H} = \sum_{i=1}^{n} (\mathbf{r}_i \wedge m_i \mathbf{v}_i), \tag{2.10}$$

where $\mathbf{v}_i = d\mathbf{r}_i/dt$. Therefore, by differentiation with respect to t,

$$\frac{d\mathbf{H}}{dt} = \sum_{i=1}^{n} \left\{ \frac{d\mathbf{r}_i}{dt} \wedge m_i \mathbf{v}_i + \mathbf{r}_i \wedge \frac{d}{dt}(m_i \mathbf{v}_i) \right\}$$

$$= \sum_{i=1}^{n} \mathbf{r}_i \wedge \mathbf{F}_i. \tag{2.11}$$

That is, the rate of change of total angular momentum about O is equal to the vector sum of the moments of the forces about O. If the latter is zero, then $\mathbf{H} = $ constant.

2.4   Partial Differentiation of Vectors

If $\mathbf{a} = \mathbf{a}(u, v)$ is a vector function of two scalar variables u, v, then

$$\frac{\partial \mathbf{a}}{\partial u} = \lim_{\Delta u \to 0} \frac{\mathbf{a}(u + \Delta u, v) - \mathbf{a}(u, v)}{\Delta u}, \qquad \frac{\partial \mathbf{a}}{\partial v} = \lim_{\Delta v \to 0} \frac{\mathbf{a}(u, v + \Delta v) - \mathbf{a}(u, v)}{\Delta v}$$

are called the partial derivatives of $\mathbf{a}$ with respect to u and v respectively, provided that the limits exist. Similarly, if a vector $\mathbf{a}$ depends on any finite number of variables $u_1, u_2, \ldots, u_n$, then the partial derivative $\partial \mathbf{a}/\partial u_i$ is defined to be the ordinary derivative with respect to the particular variable u_i when the other $n-1$ independent variables are kept constant. By expressing a vector in component form, rules for partial differentiation corresponding to rules (1) to (6) of §2.3 may be obtained. In particular, (1), (2), (4), (5) and (6) are valid for scalar and vector functions of $u_1, u_2, \ldots, u_n$ if d/du is replaced by $\partial/\partial u_i$. Rule (3) is replaced by the *chain rule* of partial differentiation of vectors, namely, if $\mathbf{a} = \mathbf{a}(u_1, u_2, \ldots, u_n)$, and each variable $u_i(i = 1, \ldots, n)$ is a function of independent variables $w_1, w_2, \ldots, w_m$, then $\mathbf{a}$ is a function of $w_1, w_2, \ldots, w_m$, and for each value of $r(r = 1, 2, \ldots, m)$

$$\frac{\partial \mathbf{a}}{\partial w_r} = \frac{\partial \mathbf{a}}{\partial u_1}\frac{\partial u_1}{\partial w_r} + \frac{\partial \mathbf{a}}{\partial u_2}\frac{\partial u_2}{\partial w_r} + \ldots + \frac{\partial \mathbf{a}}{\partial u_n}\frac{\partial u_n}{\partial w_r} \tag{2.12}$$

where $\partial/\partial w_r$ denotes differentiation with respect to w_r with the other $m-1$ w's kept constant, and $\partial/\partial u_i$ denotes differentiation with respect to u_i with the other $n-1$ u's kept constant. It is sufficient for the validity of (2.12) that the partial derivatives occurring on the right hand side exist and are continuous.

2.5   Integration of Vectors

In this section, integration is regarded as an inverse operation to differentiation. If $\mathbf{a}(u)$ is any vector function of a scalar variable u, and possesses a derivative

$$\frac{d\mathbf{a}}{du} = \mathbf{b}(u),$$

then we call $\mathbf{a}$ the *indefinite integral* of $\mathbf{b}$ with respect to u, and write

$$\mathbf{a} = \int \mathbf{b}(u)\, du. \tag{2.13}$$

Any continuous vector function $\mathbf{b}(u)$ may be shown to possess an indefinite integral. The integral (2.13) is defined only to within the addition of an arbitrary constant vector $\mathbf{c}$, because the derivative of $\mathbf{a} + \mathbf{c}$ is equal to the derivative of $\mathbf{a}$ when, and only when, $\mathbf{c}$ is a constant vector.

Example. Evaluate

(i) $\displaystyle\int \mathbf{c} \wedge \frac{d\mathbf{r}}{dt}\, dt,$ (ii) $\displaystyle\int \left(\mathbf{r} \cdot \frac{d\mathbf{s}}{dt} + \frac{d\mathbf{r}}{dt} \cdot \mathbf{s}\right) dt,$ (iii) $\displaystyle\int \mathbf{r} \wedge \frac{d^2\mathbf{r}}{dt^2}\, dt,$

where $\mathbf{c}$ is a constant vector, and $\mathbf{r}$ and $\mathbf{s}$ are vector functions of t.

(i) Since

$$\frac{d}{dt}(\mathbf{c} \wedge \mathbf{r}) = \frac{d\mathbf{c}}{dt} \wedge \mathbf{r} + \mathbf{c} \wedge \frac{d\mathbf{r}}{dt} = \mathbf{c} \wedge \frac{d\mathbf{r}}{dt},$$

therefore

$$\int \mathbf{c} \wedge \frac{d\mathbf{r}}{dt}\, dt = \mathbf{c} \wedge \mathbf{r} + \mathbf{d}$$

(ii) The integrand is the derivative with respect to t of $\mathbf{r} \cdot \mathbf{s}$, and so

$$\int \left(\mathbf{r} \cdot \frac{d\mathbf{s}}{dt} + \frac{d\mathbf{r}}{dt} \cdot \mathbf{s} \right) dt = \mathbf{r} \cdot \mathbf{s} + k.$$

(iii) Since

$$\frac{d}{dt}\left(\mathbf{r} \wedge \frac{d\mathbf{r}}{dt} \right) = \frac{d\mathbf{r}}{dt} \wedge \frac{d\mathbf{r}}{dt} + \mathbf{r} \wedge \frac{d^2\mathbf{r}}{dt^2} = \mathbf{r} \wedge \frac{d^2\mathbf{r}}{dt^2},$$

therefore

$$\int \mathbf{r} \wedge \frac{d^2\mathbf{r}}{dt^2}\, dt = \mathbf{r} \wedge \frac{d\mathbf{r}}{dt} + \mathbf{d}.$$

In the above examples, $\mathbf{d}$ denotes an arbitrary constant vector and k an arbitrary constant scalar.

EXERCISES

In the following, a dot above a symbol denotes differentiation with respect to t.

1. If $\mathbf{a}(u) = e^u\mathbf{i} + u^2\mathbf{j} - ue^{2u}\mathbf{k}$, find

$$\text{(i) } \frac{d\mathbf{a}}{du}, \quad \text{(ii) } \frac{d}{du}(\mathbf{a} \cdot \mathbf{k}), \quad \text{(iii) } \frac{d}{du}\left(\mathbf{a} \wedge \frac{d\mathbf{a}}{du} \right).$$

2. Given that $\mathbf{a} = 2\cos t\,\mathbf{i} + \sin t\,\mathbf{j}$, $\mathbf{b} = \mathbf{i} + t\mathbf{j} + t^2\mathbf{k}$, evaluate

$$\text{(i) } \frac{d}{dt}(\mathbf{a} \cdot \mathbf{b}), \quad \text{(ii) } \frac{d}{dt}(\mathbf{a} \wedge \mathbf{b}) \text{ at } t = 0, \quad \text{(iii) } \frac{d}{dt}\{\mathbf{a} \cdot (\mathbf{b} \wedge \mathbf{i})\}.$$

3. The position vector of a particle at time t is

$$\mathbf{r} = a(\cos t\,\mathbf{i} + \sin t\,\mathbf{j}) + bt\mathbf{k},$$

where a and b are constants. Find the velocity and acceleration vectors at time t, and show that $\mathbf{r} \cdot \ddot{\mathbf{r}}$ and $\ddot{\mathbf{r}} + \dot{\mathbf{r}}$ are both constant, and that $\mathbf{r} \cdot \ddot{\mathbf{r}} = 0$.

4. If $\mathbf{r}$ denotes $x\mathbf{i} + y\mathbf{j} + z\mathbf{k}$, determine $\partial r/\partial x$ and $\partial \mathbf{r}/\partial x$, and hence show that

$$\frac{\partial}{\partial x}(r^2\mathbf{r}) = 2xr + r^2\mathbf{i}.$$

5. Differentiate $|\mathbf{a} \wedge \mathbf{b}|$ with respect to t, where $\mathbf{a}$ and $\mathbf{b}$ are given differentiable vector functions of t. (Note: $|\mathbf{a} \wedge \mathbf{b}| = \{(\mathbf{a} \wedge \mathbf{b}) \cdot (\mathbf{a} \wedge \mathbf{b})\}^{\frac{1}{2}}$.)

6.   If $\dot{\mathbf{r}} = \boldsymbol{\omega} \wedge \mathbf{r}$, where $\boldsymbol{\omega}$ is a constant vector, show that $\ddot{\mathbf{r}} = -\omega^2\mathbf{r}$. Show also that

$$\frac{d}{dt}(\mathbf{r} \wedge \dot{\mathbf{r}}) = 0$$

if and only if $\boldsymbol{\omega}$ is perpendicular to $\mathbf{r}$, or $\boldsymbol{\omega}$ is parallel (or opposed) to $\mathbf{r}$.

7.   Show that $\mathbf{r} = \mathbf{a}\cos nt + \mathbf{b}\sin nt$, where $\mathbf{a}$ and $\mathbf{b}$ are arbitrary constant vectors, is a solution of the differential equation $\ddot{\mathbf{r}} = -n^2\mathbf{r}$, n being a given constant. Why must this be the general solution? Find the particular solution satisfying the conditions $\mathbf{r} = \mathbf{i}$, $\dot{\mathbf{r}} = \mathbf{j}$ at $t = 0$.

8.   If $\ddot{\mathbf{r}} = -n^2\mathbf{r}$, where $n =$ constant (motion under a central restoring force obeying Hooke's law), show that (i) $\mathbf{r} \wedge \ddot{\mathbf{r}} = 0$,   (ii) $\mathbf{r} \wedge \dot{\mathbf{r}} = \mathbf{c}$ (a constant vector),   (iii) the motion takes place in a fixed plane, (use (ii)), (iv) $\dot{r}^2 + n^2 r^2$ is constant. (Consider $d(\dot{\mathbf{r}} \cdot \dot{\mathbf{r}})/dt$.)

9.   If $\mathbf{r}$ is a function of t and $\mathbf{a}$ is a constant vector, integrate with respect to t, (i) $\mathbf{a} \wedge \ddot{\mathbf{r}}$, (ii) $\dot{\mathbf{r}} \wedge \ddot{\mathbf{r}}$, (iii) $(\ddot{\mathbf{r}} - \dot{r}\dot{\mathbf{r}})/r$. (For (iii), consider $d\hat{\mathbf{r}}/dt$.)

10.   Evaluate $\int_0^1 \mathbf{a}(u)\, du$, where $\mathbf{a}(u)$ is the vector in exercise 1.

11.   In a cloud of dust, the velocity of a typical particle, whose position is (x, y, z) at time t, is $\mathbf{v} = x^2 t\mathbf{i} - 2yz\mathbf{j} + y^2 t^2\mathbf{k}$. By using the fact that x, y and z are functions of t, show that the acceleration $d\mathbf{v}/dt$ of any particle at time $t = 0$ is $x_0^2\mathbf{i} + 4y_0 z_0^2\mathbf{j}$, where (x_0, y_0, z_0) is its position at that time.

CHAPTER 3

Scalar and Vector Fields. Integration

3.1   Scalar and Vector Fields

When a particular scalar (or vector) is associated with each point of a region of space, we say that a *scalar* (or *vector*) *field* is defined in the region. An alternative terminology for a field quantity is a *point function*.

Examples of scalar fields are the atmospheric pressure, the mass-density in a given fluid, and the temperature within the earth; examples of vector fields are the local velocity of a given fluid in motion, the gravitational force on a test particle placed anywhere in a laboratory, and the electric force (per unit volume) acting at points within an electrically charged substance.

Let x, y, z be rectangular cartesian coordinates in the region of interest. Then any scalar field will be represented by a function $\phi(x, y, z)$ giving the value of the scalar at the point (x, y, z). Conversely, any function $\phi(x, y, z)$ defines a scalar field. For example, the function $x^2 y + z^3$ defines one, since at any point (x_0, y_0, z_0) its value $x_0^2 y_0 + z_0^3$ is a scalar. A scalar may depend on other quantities, such as time, as well as on position, and the notation $\phi(x, y, z, t)$ denotes a *time dependent* scalar field.

In a similar way, $\mathbf{F}(x, y, z)$ denotes a vector field in a given region. At each point (x, y, z), the field may be expressed in component form $\mathbf{F} = F_x \mathbf{i} + F_y \mathbf{j} + F_z \mathbf{k}$, where the components F_x, F_y and F_z are each functions of x, y and z. Conversely, any vector function $F_x(x, y, z)\mathbf{i} + F_y(x, y, z)\mathbf{j} + F_z(x, y, z)\mathbf{k}$ defines a vector field. Of course, we may also consider time dependent vector fields, and use the notation $\mathbf{F}(x, y, z, t)$ for these.

Example. Sketch the two dimensional vector fields

(i) $\mathbf{F} = y^2 \mathbf{i} + \mathbf{j}$;

42

(ii) $\mathbf{G} = -\dfrac{y}{\sqrt{(x^2+y^2)}}\mathbf{i} + \dfrac{x}{\sqrt{(x^2+y^2)}}\mathbf{j},$ $\{(x,y) \neq (0,0)\}.$

(i) The components of **F** are independent of x, and the y component is constant. By substituting a few particular values for y, we easily obtain Fig. 3.1.

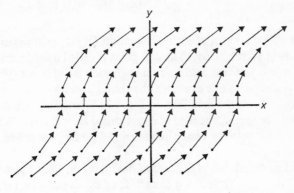

Fig. 3.1

(ii) Note that $|\mathbf{G}| = 1$ and that **G** is orthogonal to the vector $x\mathbf{i}+y\mathbf{j}$ from the origin to the field point (x,y). Further, $G_y = x/\sqrt{(x^2+y^2)}$ has the same sign as x. From these considerations we arrive at Fig. 3.2.

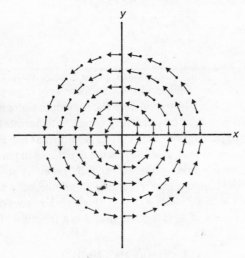

Fig. 3.2

Exercise. Sketch the vector fields

$$\text{(i)} \quad y\mathbf{i}, \qquad \text{(ii)} \quad -y\mathbf{i}+x\mathbf{j}, \qquad \text{(iii)} \quad xy\mathbf{i}-x^2\mathbf{j},$$

$$\text{(iv)} \quad \frac{x\mathbf{i}+y\mathbf{j}}{\sqrt{(x^2+y^2)}}, \qquad (x,y) \neq (0,0),$$

$$\text{(v)} \quad \frac{x\mathbf{i}+y\mathbf{j}+z\mathbf{k}}{\sqrt{(x^2+y^2+z^2)}}, \qquad (x,y,z) \neq (0,0,0).$$

A curve whose tangent at each of its points (x,y,z) is in the direction of a given field vector $\mathbf{F}(x,y,z)$ at that point is called a *field line* of $\mathbf{F}$. In general, there is just one field line through each point in a region containing a vector field. For example, the circles in the xy plane, with the origin as centre, are the field lines in Fig. 3.2. When the particular field vector is a force vector, the field lines are called *lines of force*. When the field vector is the velocity vector in a moving fluid they are called *lines of flow* or *streamlines*.

It should be noted that in the case of fluid motion, when the motion is *steady* (i.e. the velocity vector $\mathbf{q}$ at each fixed space point (x,y,z) in the fluid is independent of time) the streamlines do not vary. The streamlines then coincide with the paths of individual particles of the fluid. But this is *not* the case in unsteady motion, when the streamlines vary in time, because at any instant each streamline is formed by elements of the pathlines of an infinity of *different* fluid particles. The pathline of any one particle is traced out by the particle over a period of time, during which the pattern of streamlines is changing.

3.2   Line Integrals

In the study of scalar and vector fields we are concerned with the properties of physical fields and the way these vary from point to point and in time. This leads us to consider the differentiation and integration of field quantities. It is convenient to start with integration, and the simplest type of integration which arises is known as *line integration*.

Let $x = x(u)$, $y = y(u)$, $z = z(u)$ be the equations in parametric form of a curve C which joins points A and B, given by $u = u_0$, $u = u_1$ respectively, and suppose that u increases monotonically as the curve is described from A to B. Then, if $\phi(x,y,z)$ is a scalar function of position defined at all points of C, it follows that ϕ is a function of u on C. The integral

$$\int_{u_0}^{u_1} \phi(x(u),\,y(u),\,z(u))\,du, \tag{3.1}$$

when it exists, is called the *line integral* of ϕ with respect to u from A to B along the curve C. If the same curve is described in the opposite direction, from B to A, then the corresponding integral with respect to u is defined as

$$\int_{u_1}^{u_0} \phi \, du = -\int_{u_0}^{u_1} \phi \, du. \tag{3.2}$$

Sometimes we have to deal with line integrals around *closed* curves, so that the points A and B coincide. In this case the notation

$$\oint_C \phi \, du$$

is often used in place of (3.1), the sense of description of C being that in which u increases unless otherwise stated.

In a similar way, the line integral of a vector function $\mathbf{F}(x, y, z)$ which is defined at all points of C can be considered. Let $\mathbf{F} = F_x\mathbf{i} + F_y\mathbf{j} + F_z\mathbf{k}$, where $F_x = F_x(x, y, z)$, etc. Denote $F_x(x(u), y(u), z(u))$, $F_y(x(u), y(u), z(u))$, and $F_z(x(u), y(u), z(u))$ by $F_1(u)$, $F_2(u)$, $F_2(u)$ respectively. The *line integral* of $\mathbf{F}$ with respect to u from A to B along the curve C is by definition the vector

$$\left\{\int_{u_0}^{u_1} F_1(u) \, du\right\}\mathbf{i} + \left\{\int_{u_0}^{u_1} F_2(u) \, du\right\}\mathbf{j} + \left\{\int_{u_0}^{u_1} F_3(u) \, du\right\}\mathbf{k}.$$

if the separate integrals exist.

Example. (i) Evaluate $\int \mathbf{F} \, du$ along the curve C: $x = au^2$, $y = 2au$, $z = bu$ $(0 \leqslant u \leqslant 1)$ where u is increasing along C, a, b are constants, and $\mathbf{F}$ is the vector $yz\mathbf{i} + 2\mathbf{j} - x\mathbf{k}$. (ii) Evaluate $\int \mathbf{F} \, dx$ along the same curve.

(i) In terms of the parameter u, we have $\mathbf{F} = 2abu^2\mathbf{i} + 2\mathbf{j} - au^2\mathbf{k}$. Hence the required line integral is

$$\int_0^1 \mathbf{F} \, du = 2ab\left(\int_0^1 u^2 \, du\right)\mathbf{i} + 2\left(\int_0^1 du\right)\mathbf{j} - a\left(\int_0^1 u^2 \, du\right)\mathbf{k}$$

$$= \tfrac{2}{3}ab\mathbf{i} + 2\mathbf{j} - \tfrac{1}{3}a\mathbf{k}.$$

(ii) Here, x plays the role of the parameter u. By applying a standard formula for change of variable in elementary calculus we have

$$\int \mathbf{F} \, dx = \left(\int F_x \, dx\right)\mathbf{i} + \left(\int F_y \, dx\right)\mathbf{j} + \left(\int F_z \, dx\right)\mathbf{k},$$

$$= \left(\int F_x \frac{dx}{du} \, du\right)\mathbf{i} + \left(\int F_y \frac{dx}{du} \, du\right)\mathbf{j} + \left(\int F_z \frac{dx}{du} \, du\right)\mathbf{k},$$

where in the first line F_x, F_y, F_z are to be thought of as functions of x along C, and in the second line as functions of u, as in (i). In each case, the limits are those appropriate to the parameter employed. Since $dx/du = 2au$, we get

$$\int_C \mathbf{F}\, dx = 4a^2b\left(\int_0^1 u^3\, du\right)\mathbf{i} + 4a\left(\int_0^1 u\, du\right)\mathbf{j} - 2a^2\left(\int_0^1 u^3\, du\right)\mathbf{k}$$

$$= a^2b\mathbf{i} + 2a\mathbf{j} - \tfrac{1}{2}a^2\mathbf{k}$$

where the notation C below the integral sign is used to indicate the curve of integration.

If an integral such as $\int \mathbf{F}\, dx$ is to be evaluated over a curve C along which x does not increase or decrease monotonically, then it is interpreted as the sum of integrals over segments of C, which is subdivided so that x has the required behaviour along each segment. In evaluating the integral, we may alternatively use a substitution to replace x by a new variable which varies monotonically along the whole of C. For example, if C is a circle in the xy plane, with centre at the origin and radius a, described anticlockwise, then the substitution $x = a\cos\theta$ $(0 \leqslant \theta \leqslant 2\pi)$ would be a suitable choice.

3.3   The Tangential Line Integral of a Vector

The most important form of line integral involving a vector is the integral of its tangential component with respect to arc distance along a curve. It arises, for example, in connection with the work done by a force $\mathbf{F}$ acting on a particle which moves from a point A to a point B

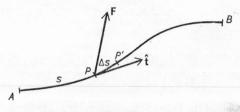

Fig. 3.3

along a curve C. Let P, P' denote neighbouring positions of the particle and let Δs denote the arc length PP', s being the arc length AP. The work done by $\mathbf{F}$ when the particle moves along the element of curve PP' is given approximately by $\mathbf{F}.\hat{\mathbf{t}}\,\Delta s$, where $\mathbf{F}$ is evaluated at P and $\hat{\mathbf{t}}$ is the unit tangent vector at P in the direction s increasing, because $\mathbf{F}.\hat{\mathbf{t}}$ is simply the resolved component of $\mathbf{F}$ in the direction $\hat{\mathbf{t}}$ (Fig. 3.3). Therefore if the entire curve is divided into elements Δs, the total amount of work done by $\mathbf{F}$ in the motion from A to B is approximately

$$\sum_{\text{all } \Delta s} \mathbf{F}.\hat{\mathbf{t}} \, \Delta s. \tag{3.3}$$

By taking a sequence of such sums with increasingly fine subdivision of C, we successively improve the approximation, and if the sum (3.3) tends to a unique limit as all $\Delta s \to 0$ (independently of the manner of subdivision) then the expression for work done takes the form of the integral

$$\lim_{\text{all } \Delta s \to 0} \sum_{\Delta s} \mathbf{F}.\hat{\mathbf{t}} \, \Delta s = \int_0^{s_1} \mathbf{F}.\hat{\mathbf{t}} \, ds, \tag{3.4}$$

where s_1 is the arc length AB. Because $\mathbf{F}.\hat{\mathbf{t}}$ is a scalar function of s, this is an ordinary definite integral and can be evaluated in the usual way, when $\mathbf{F}$ and the curve C are specified. The integral (3.4) is known as the *tangential line integral* of $\mathbf{F}$ from A to B along the curve C.

Let $\mathbf{r} = (x, y, z)$ be the position vector of P relative to the origin. We may replace $\hat{\mathbf{t}} \, \Delta s$ in the above approximation by the vector $\Delta \mathbf{r} = \overrightarrow{PP'}$, and on taking the limit as before, we are led to write the tangential line integral (3.4) in the form

$$\int_{C \, A}^{B} \mathbf{F}.d\mathbf{r} = \int_{C \, A}^{B} (F_x \, dx + F_y \, dy + F_z \, dz). \tag{3.5}$$

Here, $d\mathbf{r}$ is a differential vector whose rectangular components are the differentials dx, dy, dz (see appendix). The evaluation of (3.5) is straightforward when C is specified, since x, y and z are then known functions of a single parameter along the curve.

Example. Evaluate the tangential line integrals of the vector functions

(i) $\mathbf{F} = xy\mathbf{i} - y^2\mathbf{j} + yz\mathbf{k}$,   (ii) $\mathbf{G} = 2xy\mathbf{i} + (x^2 + z)\mathbf{j} + (y + z^2)\mathbf{k}$

along the curve C whose parametric equations are $x = a\cos t, y = a\sin t$, $z = bt$, where a and b are positive constants and t increases from 0 to 2π.

(i) The curve is part of the helix shown in Fig. 2.2, the initial and terminal points being $A = (1, 0, 0)$ and $B = (1, 0, 2\pi b)$ respectively. From the given parametric equations for C, we have

$$dx = -a\sin t \, dt, \quad dy = a\cos t \, dt, \quad dz = b \, dt$$

and so

$$\int_{C\,A}^{B} \mathbf{F} \cdot d\mathbf{r} = \int_{C\,A}^{B} (xy\,dx - y^2\,dy + yz\,dz)$$

$$= \int_{0}^{2\pi} (-a^3\cos t \sin^2 t\,dt - a^3\sin^2 t \cos t\,dt + ab^2 t \sin t\,dt)$$

$$= a \int_{0}^{2\pi} (-2a^2\sin^2 t \cos t + b^2 t \sin t)\,dt$$

$$= -2\pi ab^2,$$

on performing the integration.

(ii) Clearly, this integral could be calculated in the same way, but note the following alternative approach. Let $f(x, y, z)$ be the scalar function $(x^2 + z)y + \frac{1}{3}z^3$. We have for the components of $\mathbf{G}$:

$$G_x = 2xy = \frac{\partial f}{\partial x}, \qquad G_y = x^2 + z = \frac{\partial f}{\partial y}, \qquad G_z = y + z^2 = \frac{\partial f}{\partial z}. \qquad (3.6)$$

Therefore

$$\int_{C\,A}^{B} \mathbf{G} \cdot d\mathbf{r} = \int_{C\,A}^{B} (G_x\,dx + G_y\,dy + G_z\,dz)$$

$$= \int_{C\,A}^{B} \left(\frac{\partial f}{\partial x}dx + \frac{\partial f}{\partial y}dy + \frac{\partial f}{\partial z}dz \right)$$

$$= \int_{C\,A}^{B} df$$

$$= \left| f \right|_{A}^{B}$$

$$= \left| (x^2 + z)y + \frac{1}{3}z^3 \right|_{(1,0,0)}^{(1,0,2\pi b)}$$

$$= \frac{1}{3}(2\pi b)^3 = \frac{8}{3}\pi^3 b^3,$$

where we have employed the chain rule for differentials (appendix).

In (ii), the calculation was found to depend only on the value of f at the points A and B, and not on the particular path of integration C joining these points. Whenever a vector is of the form

$$\mathbf{G} = \left(\frac{\partial f}{\partial x}, \frac{\partial f}{\partial y}, \frac{\partial f}{\partial z} \right), \qquad (3.7)$$

where f is a single valued function of x, y, z in a given region, then the tangential line integral of $\mathbf{G}$ has the same value for all paths in the region with the same initial and terminal points. This special case is of great importance and will be discussed in more detail later.

How is the function f determined, assuming it exists? For the particular vector $\mathbf{G}$ in (ii) above, we have to satisfy the relations (3.6). From the first of these we get, on integration with respect to x,

$$f = x^2y + g(y, z), \tag{3.8}$$

where $g(y, z)$ is a function of integration to be determined. On substituting (3.8) into the second of the relations (3.6) we find

$$\frac{\partial f}{\partial y} = x^2 + \frac{\partial g}{\partial y} = x^2 + z,$$

so that

$$\frac{\partial g}{\partial y} = z,$$

and on integrating with respect to y (and noting that g is a function of y and z only)

$$g = yz + h(z),$$

where $h(z)$ is to be determined. We thus have by (3.8)

$$f = x^2y + yz + h(z),$$

and on substituting this expression into the last of the relations (3.6) we obtain

$$\frac{\partial f}{\partial z} = y + \frac{dh}{dz} = y + z^2,$$

whence

$$h = \tfrac{1}{3}z^3 + \text{constant}. \tag{3.9}$$

The particular function $f = (x^2 + z)y + \tfrac{1}{3}z^3$ used above is obtained by choosing the constant in (3.9) to be zero.

The tangential line integral of the vector $\mathbf{F}$ in (i) is *not* independent of the path joining the given points A and B. For example, if we replace C by the straight line path AB, which is parallel to the z axis, we may write $d\mathbf{r} = dz\,\mathbf{k}$ since $dx = dy = 0$, and so

$$\int_A^B \mathbf{F} \cdot d\mathbf{r} = \int_A^B F_z\,dz = \int_A^B yz\,dz = 0,$$

since $y = 0$ everywhere on the path. This is not the same as the result found for the path C. The reader should attempt the construction of a function $f(x, y, z)$ such that

$$\mathbf{F} = \left(\frac{\partial f}{\partial x}, \frac{\partial f}{\partial y}, \frac{\partial f}{\partial z} \right)$$

and see where the construction breaks down.

D

3.4 Some Further Types of Line Integral

In addition to the types of line integral met so far, there are other possibilities. For example, if $\phi(x, y, z)$ is a scalar point function and $\mathbf{F}(x, y, z)$ a vector point function defined at all points of a curve C, then by definition

$$\int_C \phi \, d\mathbf{r} = \int_C \phi(dx\,\mathbf{i} + dy\,\mathbf{j} + dz\,\mathbf{k})$$

$$= \left(\int_C \phi \, dx\right)\mathbf{i} + \left(\int_C \phi \, dy\right)\mathbf{j} + \left(\int_C \phi \, dz\right)\mathbf{k} \qquad (3.10)$$

and

$$\int_C \mathbf{F} \wedge d\mathbf{r} = \int_C (F_y\,dz - F_z\,dy)\mathbf{i} + \int_C (F_z\,dx - F_x\,dz)\mathbf{j} + \int_C (F_x\,dy - F_y\,dx)\mathbf{k}. \qquad (3.11)$$

In each case, the integration reduces to the evaluation of ordinary integrals when x, y and z are each expressed in terms of a single parameter u, using the parametric equations $x = x(u)$, $y = y(u)$, $z = z(u)$ of the curve C.

An example of (3.11) is afforded in physics by the expression

$$-I \int_C \mathbf{B} \wedge d\mathbf{r}$$

for the resultant force on a wire loop C which carries a uniform current I and is situated in a magnetic field of induction $\mathbf{B}$ (in rationalized m.k.s. or S.I. units).

3.5 Surfaces

A surface in 3-dimensional space is a set of points $\mathbf{r} = \mathbf{r}(u, v)$ which depend on two parameters u and v. In terms of rectangular cartesian coordinates we have

$$x = x(u, v), \qquad y = y(u, v), \qquad z = z(u, v). \qquad (3.12)$$

Under reasonable analytic conditions we can in principle eliminate u and v in (3.12) to obtain one relation of the form

$$z = z(x, y), \quad \text{or} \quad x = x(y, z), \quad \text{or} \quad y = y(z, x), \qquad (3.13)$$

where we are in each case using two of the three cartesian coordinates themselves as parameters. Again, the *implicit* form of equation for a surface

$$\phi(x, y, z) = \text{constant}$$

is equivalent to (3.13), assuming that we can solve for any one of the variables x, y and z in terms of the other two.

The parameters u and v in (3.12) act as coordinates for points on the given surface. The lines $u = $ constant and $v = $ constant are *parametric lines* or *coordinate lines*, and since these are in general curved, the coordinates u, v are called *curvilinear coordinates* for the surface (Fig. 3.4).

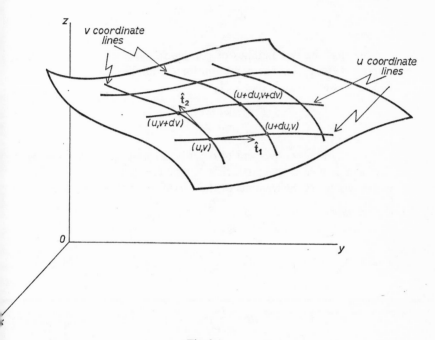

Fig. 3.4

Suppose v is kept constant, and a differential displacement is made along the u coordinate line from the point (u, v) to the point $(u + du, v)$. By taking differentials in (3.12), it follows that the vector with components

$$dx = \frac{\partial x}{\partial u}du, \qquad dy = \frac{\partial y}{\partial u}du, \qquad dz = \frac{\partial z}{\partial u}du \qquad (3.14)$$

represents a corresponding displacement along the tangent to the u

coordinate line in the direction u increasing. Therefore, if we write

$$\frac{\partial \mathbf{r}}{\partial u} = \left(\frac{\partial x}{\partial u}, \frac{\partial y}{\partial u}, \frac{\partial z}{\partial u}\right)$$

we have that the *unit* tangent vector to the surface in the direction u increasing is

$$\hat{\mathbf{t}}_1 = \frac{\partial \mathbf{r}}{\partial u} \bigg/ \left|\frac{\partial \mathbf{r}}{\partial u}\right|.$$

Similarly the unit tangent vector in the direction v increasing is

$$\hat{\mathbf{t}}_2 = \frac{\partial \mathbf{r}}{\partial v} \bigg/ \left|\frac{\partial \mathbf{r}}{\partial v}\right|.$$

Note that the two families of parametric lines intersect at angle α, where $\cos \alpha = \hat{\mathbf{t}}_1 . \hat{\mathbf{t}}_2$. The condition for the families to intersect orthogonally at each point is that $\hat{\mathbf{t}}_1 . \hat{\mathbf{t}}_2 = 0$, i.e.

$$\frac{\partial \mathbf{r}}{\partial u} . \frac{\partial \mathbf{r}}{\partial v} = 0. \qquad (3.15)$$

It is sometimes convenient to describe a surface in yet another way. Consider a pair of neighbouring points $P(u,v)$ and $P'(u+du, v+dv)$ where du, dv are differentials of the curvilinear coordinates u, v. When du and dv are small, the vector $\overrightarrow{PP'}$ is approximated by the displacement $d\mathbf{r} = (dx, dy, dz)$ along the tangent plane at P where

$$dx = \frac{\partial x}{\partial u} du + \frac{\partial x}{\partial v} dv, \qquad dy = \frac{\partial y}{\partial u} du + \frac{\partial y}{\partial v} dv, \qquad dz = \frac{\partial z}{\partial u} du + \frac{\partial z}{\partial v} dv,$$

that is,

$$d\mathbf{r} = \frac{\partial \mathbf{r}}{\partial u} du + \frac{\partial \mathbf{r}}{\partial v} dv. \qquad (3.16)$$

The length of this vector is denoted by ds, so that

$$ds^2 = d\mathbf{r} . d\mathbf{r}$$

$$= \left(\frac{\partial \mathbf{r}}{\partial u} du + \frac{\partial \mathbf{r}}{\partial v} dv\right) . \left(\frac{\partial \mathbf{r}}{\partial u} du + \frac{\partial \mathbf{r}}{\partial v} dv\right)$$

$$= \left(\frac{\partial \mathbf{r}}{\partial u}\right)^2 du^2 + 2\frac{\partial \mathbf{r}}{\partial u} . \frac{\partial \mathbf{r}}{\partial v} du dv + \left(\frac{\partial \mathbf{r}}{\partial v}\right)^2 dv^2. \qquad (3.17)$$

On the right hand side of (3.17), the coefficients of du^2, $du dv$ and dv^2 are expressible as functions of u, v only, and so ds^2 is expressed in the form (and in a standard notation)

$$ds^2 = g_{11}(u, v)\, du^2 + 2g_{12}(u, v)\, du\, dv + g_{22}(u, v)\, dv^2 \qquad (3.18)$$

which is called the *metric* or *square of the line element* for the surface. The quantities g_{11}, g_{22}, g_{12} and g_{21} (defined to be equal to g_{12}) are the elements of a symmetric matrix called the *metric tensor*, and determine the geometrical properties of the surface near any point. We note that the coordinate lines meet orthogonally if and only if $g_{12} = 0$.

3.6 Cylindrical Polar and Spherical Polar Coordinates

In many problems involving surfaces and 3-dimensional regions it is convenient to use *polar* coordinates.

Cylindrical Polar Coordinates R, ψ, z are as shown in Fig. 3.5, and are related to rectangular cartesian coordinates x, y, z by the equations

$$x = R\cos\psi, \qquad y = R\sin\psi, \qquad z = z. \qquad (3.19)$$

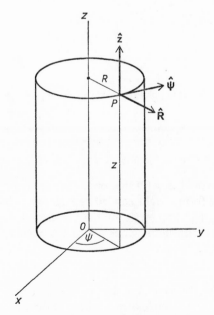

Fig. 3.5. P is the point (R, ψ, z) in cylindrical polar coordinates.

The ranges of these coordinates are

$$R \geqslant 0, \qquad 0 \leqslant \psi < 2\pi, \qquad -\infty < z < \infty.$$

The unit vectors $\hat{\mathbf{R}}, \hat{\boldsymbol{\psi}}, \hat{\mathbf{z}}$ in the directions of R, ψ and z increasing, respectively, are mutually orthogonal and, taken in that order, form a right handed system at each point.

Spherical Polar Coordinates r, θ, ψ are as shown in Fig. 3.6, and are related to rectangular cartesian coordinates x, y, z by the equations

$$x = r\sin\theta\cos\psi, \qquad y = r\sin\theta\sin\psi, \qquad z = r\cos\theta. \qquad (3.20)$$

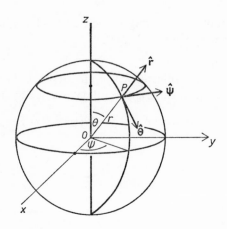

Fig. 3.6. P is the point (r, θ, ψ) in spherical polar coordinates.

The ranges of these coordinates are

$$r \geqslant 0, \qquad 0 \leqslant \psi < 2\pi, \qquad 0 \leqslant \theta \leqslant \pi,$$

and the unit vectors $\hat{\mathbf{r}}, \hat{\boldsymbol{\theta}}, \hat{\boldsymbol{\psi}}$ (in that order) in the respective directions of r, θ, ψ increasing form a right handed orthogonal system at each point.

Since $r^2 = x^2 + y^2 + z^2$ by (3.20), the use made here of the symbol r is not in conflict with its previous use as the magnitude of the vector $\mathbf{r} = (x, y, z)$.

Example. Let the sphere in Fig. 3.6 have radius a. Find the cartesian components of the unit tangent vectors in the directions θ, ψ increasing, and determine the line element for the sphere in terms of θ and ψ.

We have that $\hat{\boldsymbol{\theta}}$ is parallel to the vector

$$\frac{\partial \mathbf{r}}{\partial \theta} = \frac{\partial x}{\partial \theta}\mathbf{i} + \frac{\partial y}{\partial \theta}\mathbf{j} + \frac{\partial z}{\partial \theta}\mathbf{k}$$

$$= a\cos\theta\cos\psi\,\mathbf{i} + a\cos\theta\sin\psi\,\mathbf{j} - a\sin\theta\,\mathbf{k}, \tag{3.21}$$

by (3.20) with r put equal to a. The magnitude of this vector is a, as is found by squaring and adding the components, and so the unit vector $\hat{\boldsymbol{\theta}}$ has components

$$\hat{\boldsymbol{\theta}}: \quad (\cos\theta\cos\psi, \cos\theta\sin\psi, -\sin\theta). \tag{3.22}$$

Similarly, $\hat{\boldsymbol{\psi}}$ is parallel to the vector

$$\frac{\partial \mathbf{r}}{\partial \psi} = \frac{\partial x}{\partial \psi}\mathbf{i} + \frac{\partial y}{\partial \psi}\mathbf{j} + \frac{\partial z}{\partial \psi}\mathbf{k}$$

$$= -a\sin\theta\sin\psi\,\mathbf{i} + a\sin\theta\cos\psi\,\mathbf{j}, \tag{3.23}$$

by (3.20). The magnitude of this vector is found by inspection to be $a\sin\theta$ ($\sin\theta \geqslant 0$ in $0 \leqslant \theta \leqslant \pi$) and so the unit vector $\hat{\boldsymbol{\psi}}$ has components

$$\hat{\boldsymbol{\psi}}: \quad (-\sin\psi, \cos\psi, 0). \tag{3.24}$$

These expressions, (3.22) and (3.24), may be verified by resolving the unit vectors $\hat{\boldsymbol{\theta}}$ and $\hat{\boldsymbol{\psi}}$ along the x, y and z directions using Fig. (3.6).

The required line element is ds, where

$$ds^2 = \left(\frac{\partial \mathbf{r}}{\partial \theta}\right)^2 d\theta^2 + 2\frac{\partial \mathbf{r}}{\partial \theta}\cdot\frac{\partial \mathbf{r}}{\partial \psi}d\theta d\psi + \left(\frac{\partial \mathbf{r}}{\partial \psi}\right)^2 d\psi^2$$

$$= a^2\,d\theta^2 + a^2\sin^2\theta\,d\psi^2.$$

Exercise. Show that the unit vectors $\hat{\mathbf{R}}, \hat{\boldsymbol{\psi}}, \hat{\mathbf{z}}$ in Fig. 3.5 have cartesian components given by

$$\hat{\mathbf{R}} = (\cos\psi, \sin\psi, 0), \qquad \hat{\boldsymbol{\psi}} = (-\sin\psi, \cos\psi, 0), \qquad \hat{\mathbf{z}} = (0, 0, 1)$$

and also that the curved surface of the cylinder in the Figure has the line element ds, where

$$ds^2 = a^2\,d\psi^2 + dz^2,$$

and a is the radius.

3.7 Surface Integrals

Let S be a surface divided in any manner into n elements of area $\Delta S_i (i = 1, 2, \ldots, n)$. Let $f(x, y, z)$ be a scalar function defined at all points of S, with value f_i at any chosen point P_i in ΔS_i. If the sum

$$\sum_{i=1}^{n} f_i \,\Delta S_i \qquad (3.25)$$

tends to a limit as the dimensions of all the ΔS_i tend to zero (and n tends to infinity), and if this limit does not depend on the manner of division of S or the particular choice of P_i in ΔS_i, then the limit is called the *surface integral* of f over S and is written

$$\int_S f \, dS \quad \text{or} \quad \iint_S f \, dS. \qquad (3.26)$$

The double integral sign is used to emphasize the fact that a surface integral usually has to be evaluated as a double integral, while the single integral sign may be used for brevity. The above limit will always exist if f is a continuous function on S and if the parametric equations of S involve only continuous functions with continuous derivatives.

As a simple example of a surface integral, suppose that a layer of matter is deposited on a given surface S, and that $\rho(x, y, z)$ is the mass of the matter per unit area in the neighbourhood of any point (x, y, z) on S. Then the total mass deposited on the surface is the surface integral $\int_S \rho \, dS$.

The evaluation of (3.26) in any particular case may be carried out by using curvilinear coordinates u, v on S. Let a typical element ΔS be formed by the elementary parallelogram bounded by the lines $u = u_0$, $u = u_0 + \Delta u$, $v = v_0$, $v = v_0 + \Delta v$, where Δu and Δv are arbitrary small positive quantities. Then in the notation of Fig. 3.7 we have approximately that

$$\Delta S = PQ \,.\, PT \sin QPT = \left| \overrightarrow{PQ} \wedge \overrightarrow{PT} \right| \qquad (3.27)$$

Now, the vector $\overrightarrow{PQ}$ is the displacement $\Delta \mathbf{r}$ from P when an increment Δu in u is made with v kept constant, and so to first order in the quantities Δu, Δv

$$\overrightarrow{PQ} = \frac{\partial \mathbf{r}}{\partial u} \Delta u, \qquad (3.28)$$

and likewise

$$\overrightarrow{PT} = \frac{\partial \mathbf{r}}{\partial v} \Delta v.$$

Therefore, by (3.27), to first order

$$\Delta S = \left| \frac{\partial \mathbf{r}}{\partial u} \wedge \frac{\partial \mathbf{r}}{\partial v} \right| \Delta u \, \Delta v.$$

On multiplying by f, evaluated at the point u, v, summing over ΔS, and proceeding to the limit as all Δu and Δv tend to zero, we get

$$\int_S f \, dS = \iint_S f(u,v) \left| \frac{\partial \mathbf{r}}{\partial u} \wedge \frac{\partial \mathbf{r}}{\partial v} \right| du dv \qquad (3.29)$$

where $f(u,v)$ is used to denote $f(x(u,v), y(u,v), z(u,v))$. The double integral on the right is in terms of u and v only, and the limits of integration will be determined by the ranges of u and v on S.

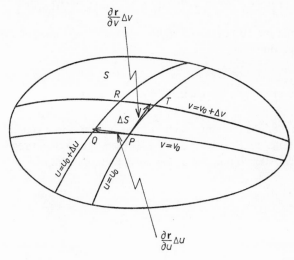

Fig. 3.7

Example. Evaluate the surface integral of the function $f = xyz$ over the positive octant of the sphere $x^2 + y^2 + z^2 = a^2$.

Introduce polar coordinates (θ, ψ) on the given surface by putting

$$x = a\sin\theta\cos\psi, \qquad y = a\sin\theta\sin\psi, \qquad z = a\cos\theta, \qquad (3.30)$$

where for the positive octant $0 \leqslant \theta \leqslant \frac{1}{2}\pi$, $0 \leqslant \psi \leqslant \frac{1}{2}\pi$. With $\mathbf{r} = (x, y, z)$, $\partial\mathbf{r}/\partial\theta$ and $\partial\mathbf{r}/\partial\psi$ are as found previously (equations 3.21, 3.23) and on forming their vector product we obtain

$$\frac{\partial \mathbf{r}}{\partial \theta} \wedge \frac{\partial \mathbf{r}}{\partial \psi} = a^2(\sin^2\theta\cos\psi\,\mathbf{i} + \sin^2\theta\sin\psi\,\mathbf{j} + \sin\theta\cos\theta\,\mathbf{k}),$$

and so

$$\left| \frac{\partial \mathbf{r}}{\partial \theta} \wedge \frac{\partial \mathbf{r}}{\partial \psi} \right| = a^2(\sin^4\theta + \sin^2\theta\cos^2\theta)^{\frac{1}{2}} = a^2\sin\theta \qquad (3.31)$$

(using $\sin^2 \theta + \cos^2 \theta = 1$); our choice of sign in taking the square root being correct since $\sin \theta \geqslant 0$ in $0 \leqslant \theta \leqslant \frac{1}{2}\pi$. Therefore, with S denoting the given surface

$$\int_S f \, dS = \int_S xyz \, dS = a^5 \int_0^{\pi/2} \int_0^{\pi/2} \sin^3\theta \cos \theta \sin \psi \cos \psi \, d\theta d\psi$$

by (3.29), (3.30) and (3.31). On carrying out the integration with respect to ψ first we get for the value of the surface integral

$$a^5 \int_0^{\pi/2} \sin^3\theta \cos \theta \left| \frac{1}{2} \sin^2\psi \right|_0^{\pi/2} d\theta = \frac{a^5}{2} \left| \frac{1}{4} \sin^4\theta \right|_0^{\pi/2} = \frac{1}{8}a^5.$$

A simpler method of obtaining the expression $a^2 \sin \theta \, d\theta d\psi$, to replace dS, is given on p. 65.

3.8   The Flux of a Vector Field through a Surface

In Fig. 3.8, $\hat{\mathbf{n}}$ is the unit normal to the surface S at a general point P and $\mathbf{F}$ denotes a field vector defined throughout a certain region which contains S. At each point of S, the normal component of $\mathbf{F}$ is the scalar

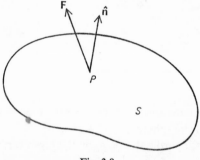

Fig. 3.8

function $\mathbf{F} \cdot \hat{\mathbf{n}}$, and the surface integral of $\mathbf{F} \cdot \hat{\mathbf{n}}$ over S is called the *flux* of $\mathbf{F}$ through S. That is,

$$\text{flux of } \mathbf{F} \text{ through } S = \int_S \mathbf{F} \cdot \hat{\mathbf{n}} \, dS. \tag{3.32}$$

The flux of a vector field through a given surface is a very important concept in physics.

Note that there is an ambiguity in sign in the definition because of the freedom of choice in the sense of direction of $\hat{\mathbf{n}}$. For a *closed* surface (i.e.

one which bounds a finite region), it is conventional to take the direction of $\hat{\mathbf{n}}$ to point away from the enclosed region, the quantity (3.32) then being known as the *outward flux* through S.

Some surfaces have only *one* side, and for these it is not possible to define flux in the above way. An example of a one-sided surface is the Möbius strip, which consists of a band with a single twist. In Fig. 3.9, we see the result of constructing a unit normal vector $\hat{\mathbf{n}}$ at one point P on a Möbius strip and then adding further normals on the 'same' side at a succession of points around the strip. When we return to P the final direction of $\hat{\mathbf{n}}$ is found to be opposed to its initial direction. The definition (3.32) applies only to two-sided or *orientable* surfaces, which are the only ones normally encountered in practical applications.

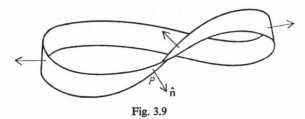

Fig. 3.9

The integral (3.32) is also written

$$\int_S \mathbf{F} . d\mathbf{S} \qquad (3.33)$$

where $d\mathbf{S}$ denotes $\hat{\mathbf{n}} dS$, i.e. $d\mathbf{S}$ is a vector equal in magnitude to the differential area element dS and having the direction of $\hat{\mathbf{n}}$.

As an example of a flux integral, consider the motion of a fluid which at some time t_0 occupies a region of space R. Let the velocity of the fluid at the point (x, y, z) in R, at time t_0, be $\mathbf{q}(x, y, z)$, and let S be any surface fixed in space and lying entirely in R. The amount of fluid passing through an element ΔS of S during a brief time interval $(t_0, t_0 + \Delta t)$ is that contained within an elementary prism whose base is ΔS and whose generators are given in length and direction by $\mathbf{q} \Delta t$ (Fig. 3.10). The volume of this prism is

$$\Delta S \times \text{perpendicular height} = \Delta S(\mathbf{q} \Delta t . \hat{\mathbf{n}})$$

and so the volume rate of flow through ΔS is $\mathbf{q} . \hat{\mathbf{n}} \Delta S$. On summing over all elements ΔS and taking the limit as all ΔS tend to zero, we get for the total volume rate of flow through S, in the sense indicated by $\hat{\mathbf{n}}$,

$$\int_S \mathbf{q} . \hat{\mathbf{n}} \, dS = \int_S \mathbf{q} . d\mathbf{S}.$$

If the mass density of the fluid at the point (x, y, z) at time t_0 is $\rho(x, y, z)$, then the total mass per unit time crossing S at time t_0 is another flux integral,

$$\int_S \rho \mathbf{q} . d\mathbf{S}.$$

This example explains the use of the term 'flux', meaning flow, for integrals of the above type.

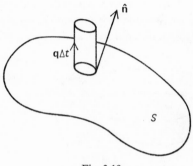

Fig. 3.10

3.9   The Evaluation of Flux Integrals

Method 1. This method is useful if the surface is expressed in the parametric form $x = x(u, v)$, $y = y(u, v)$, $z = z(u, v)$.

Example. Find the flux of the vector field $\mathbf{F} = z\mathbf{j} - \mathbf{k}$ through the surface $x = \sin u \cos v$, $y = \sin u \sin v$, $z = \cos^2 u$, where $0 \leqslant u \leqslant \frac{1}{2}\pi$, $0 \leqslant v < 2\pi$.

Tangent vectors to the surface in the directions u increasing, v increasing, respectively are $\partial \mathbf{r}/\partial u$ and $\partial \mathbf{r}/\partial v$ (p. 52), and so a normal vector $\mathbf{n}$ (not necessarily *unit*) to the surface is given by the vector product

$$\mathbf{n} = \frac{\partial \mathbf{r}}{\partial u} \wedge \frac{\partial \mathbf{r}}{\partial v}. \qquad (3.34)$$

By (3.29), a differential element of the surface is

$$dS = \left| \frac{\partial \mathbf{r}}{\partial u} \wedge \frac{\partial \mathbf{r}}{\partial v} \right| du dv. \qquad (3.35)$$

Combining (3.34) and (3.35), we get

$$dS = \hat{\mathbf{n}}\,dS = \left(\frac{\partial \mathbf{r}}{\partial u} \wedge \frac{\partial \mathbf{r}}{\partial v}\right) du\,dv, \tag{3.36}$$

since the right hand side has the same magnitude and direction as $d\mathbf{S}$. We therefore need to evaluate

$$\int_0^{\pi/2} \int_0^{2\pi} \mathbf{F} \cdot \left(\frac{\partial \mathbf{r}}{\partial u} \wedge \frac{\partial \mathbf{r}}{\partial v}\right) du\,dv, \tag{3.37}$$

where we use the convention (as elsewhere in this book) that in multiple integrals, the integral signs are written in the same order from left to right as the differentials to which they relate.

Now,

$$\frac{\partial \mathbf{r}}{\partial u} = \cos u \cos v\,\mathbf{i} + \cos u \sin v\,\mathbf{j} - 2\cos u \sin u\,\mathbf{k},$$

$$\frac{\partial \mathbf{r}}{\partial v} = -\sin u \sin v\,\mathbf{i} + \sin u \cos v\,\mathbf{j},$$

and so

$$\frac{\partial \mathbf{r}}{\partial u} \wedge \frac{\partial \mathbf{r}}{\partial v} = 2\sin^2 u \cos u \cos v\,\mathbf{i} + 2\sin^2 u \cos u \sin v\,\mathbf{j} + \sin u \cos u\,\mathbf{k}. \tag{3.38}$$

Also

$$\mathbf{F} = z\mathbf{j} - \mathbf{k} = \cos^2 u\,\mathbf{j} - \mathbf{k}.$$

Therefore, on substituting, we obtain for the flux integral (3.37),

$$\int_0^{\pi/2} \int_0^{2\pi} (2\sin^2 u \cos^3 u \sin v - \sin u \cos u)\,du\,dv.$$

The contribution to the integral from the first term in the integrand is zero, as follows if we carry out the integration with respect to v first. We thus find

$$\text{flux} = -2\pi \int_0^{\pi/2} \sin u \cos u\,du$$

$$= -2\pi \left| \tfrac{1}{2}\sin^2 u \right|_0^{\pi/2} = -\pi.$$

We have (arbitrarily) chosen the sense of direction of $\hat{\mathbf{n}}$ such that, by (3.34) and (3.38), $\hat{\mathbf{n}}$ has positive $\mathbf{k}$ component. Had we chosen the opposite direction for the normal, the value obtained for the flux would have been $+\pi$.

By eliminating u, v from the parametric equation for the given surface, we see that its cartesian equation is $x^2 + y^2 = 1 - z$. Since $x^2 + y^2$ is the square of the distance of the point (x, y, z) from the z axis, the surface is seen to be part of a *paraboloid of revolution* obtained by rotating the curve $y^2 = 1 - z$, $x = 0$ about the z axis (Fig. 3.11).

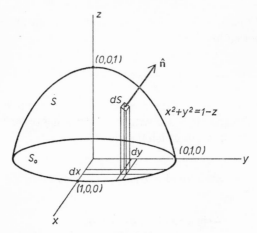

Fig. 3.11

Method 2. If the surface S is expressed in the implicit equation form $f(x, y, z) = $ constant, the following method is normally simpler in practice than the last one. It depends on the fact that a normal to the surface at any point is given by the vector $(\partial f/\partial x, \partial f/\partial y, \partial f/\partial z)$. To verify this result, consider the chain rule for differentials

$$df = \frac{\partial f}{\partial x} dx + \frac{\partial f}{\partial y} dy + \frac{\partial f}{\partial z} dz. \tag{3.39}$$

Suppose that dx, dy, dz are the components of a differential displacement $d\mathbf{r}$ from the point $P(x, y, z)$ in any direction tangential to S at P. Then since f is constant on S, we have $df = 0$ and so the right hand side of (3.39) is zero. This means that the vector $(\partial f/\partial x, \partial f/\partial y, \partial f/\partial z)$, where the partial derivatives are evaluated at the point P, is orthogonal to every direction in the tangent plane to S at P, and is therefore a normal vector to S. (For further details, see Chapter 4.)

We shall illustrate the method using again the previous example. Let dS be so chosen that its projection on the xy plane is the rectangular element $dxdy$ (Fig. 3.11). We have

$$dS \cos(\hat{\mathbf{n}}, \mathbf{k}) = dS\,\hat{\mathbf{n}} . \mathbf{k} = dxdy, \tag{3.40}$$

and

$$\int_S \mathbf{F} . \hat{\mathbf{n}} \, dS = \iint_{S_0} \frac{\mathbf{F} . \hat{\mathbf{n}}}{\mathbf{k} . \hat{\mathbf{n}}} \, dxdy. \tag{3.41}$$

where S_0 is the projection of S on the xy plane. In our case, the equation of S is $x^2+y^2+z = 1$, $z \geqslant 0$, and so S_0 is the circle $x^2+y^2 = 1$, $z = 0$ and its interior.

It is not necessary to calculate the *unit* normal vector to S, because $\hat{\mathbf{n}}$ may be replaced by $\mathbf{n}$ on the right in (3.41), where $\mathbf{n}$ is any normal vector. This is clear since the magnitude n in numerator and denominator cancels. Therefore, writing $f = x^2+y^2+z$, we may choose

$$\mathbf{n} = \frac{\partial f}{\partial x}\mathbf{i}+\frac{\partial f}{\partial y}\mathbf{j}+\frac{\partial f}{\partial z}\mathbf{k} = 2x\mathbf{i}+2y\mathbf{j}+\mathbf{k}. \tag{3.42}$$

But $\mathbf{F} = z\mathbf{j}-\mathbf{k}$,

$$\mathbf{F}.\mathbf{n} = 2yz-1 = 2y(1-x^2-y^2)-1, \tag{3.43}$$

and

$$\mathbf{k}.\mathbf{n} = 1.$$

Note that in (3.43) we replace z by its value on S, and not by its value, zero, on S_0. The required flux is therefore

$$\int_S \mathbf{F}.d\mathbf{S} = \iint_{S_0} \{2y(1-x^2-y^2)-1\}\, dxdy. \tag{3.44}$$

To simplify the evaluation of the double integral (3.44), introduce polar coordinates R, ψ in the xy plane. Then $x = R\cos\psi$, $y = R\sin\psi$, and $dxdy$ must be replaced by $R\, dRd\psi$. The flux integral (3.44) becomes on substitution for x and y

$$\int_0^1\int_0^{2\pi} \{2R(1-R^2)\sin\psi-1\}\, R\, dRd\psi.$$

By integration with respect to ψ first, we find that the contribution from the first term in the integrand is zero, and so the flux is

$$-2\pi \int_0^1 R\, dR = -2\pi(\tfrac{1}{2}) = -\pi$$

as before. This method avoids the need to calculate a vector product and is therefore simpler than method 1.

The flux will automatically be measured in the normal direction with positive $\mathbf{k}$ component, since in (3.40) $\hat{\mathbf{n}}.\mathbf{k}$ is the ratio of the two positive quantities dS and $dxdy$. This result is not affected by a subsequent change to a more general normal vector $\mathbf{n}$.

In some examples it may be more convenient to project S instead onto the yz or the zx coordinate plane. In any case, it is necessary for S to have a *simple* projection onto the plane in question (that is to say, each point of S_0 must be the projection of just *one* point of S). If the projection is not simple, then the method is still applicable provided that S can be divided into a finite number of parts which individually satisfy the condition, since the flux through each part can be calculated separately. The surface in the above example has a simple projection on the xy plane, but not on the other two coordinate planes.

Method 3. In the particular cases where the surface is a cylinder or a sphere, or part of one of these, it is quicker to express $\hat{\mathbf{n}}$ and dS in terms of polar coordinates by inspection of a diagram.

Example (i). S is the curved surface of the cylinder $x^2+y^2 = a^2$, $b \leqslant z \leqslant c$. By Fig. 3.12,

$$dS = a\, d\psi dz,$$

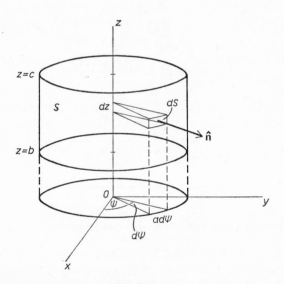

Fig. 3.12

and by resolving $\hat{\mathbf{n}}$ along the coordinate axes we have

$$\hat{\mathbf{n}} = \cos\psi\,\mathbf{i} + \sin\psi\,\mathbf{j},$$

and so for any vector field $\mathbf{F}$

$$\int\limits_{S} \mathbf{F}.\hat{\mathbf{n}}\, dS = a \int_{0}^{2\pi}\int_{b}^{c} \mathbf{F}.(\cos\psi\,\mathbf{i} + \sin\psi\,\mathbf{j})\, d\psi dz,$$

where before carrying out the integration it remains only to express the cartesian components of $\mathbf{F}$ in terms of the cylindrical polar coordinates on S by using the relations

$$x = a\cos\psi, \qquad y = a\sin\psi, \qquad z = z. \qquad (3.45)$$

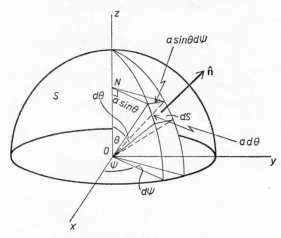

Fig. 3.13

Example (ii). S is the hemisphere $x^2 + y^2 + z^2 = a^2, \quad z \geqslant 0$. By Fig. 3.13,

$$dS = a\sin\theta\,d\psi\,.\,a\,d\theta = a^2\sin\theta\,d\theta d\psi,$$

and by resolving $\hat{\mathbf{n}}$ along the coordinate axes, we have

$$\hat{\mathbf{n}} = \cos\theta\,\mathbf{k} + \sin\theta(\cos\psi\,\mathbf{i} + \sin\psi\,\mathbf{j})$$
$$= \sin\theta\cos\psi\,\mathbf{i} + \sin\theta\sin\psi\,\mathbf{j} + \cos\theta\,\mathbf{k}. \qquad (3.46)$$

Alternatively, $\hat{\mathbf{n}}$ can be found by the method used in (3.42), using also (3.47). For any vector field $\mathbf{F}$

$$\int_S \mathbf{F}.d\mathbf{S} = a^2 \int_0^{\pi/2}\int_0^{2\pi} \mathbf{F}.(\sin\theta\cos\psi\,\mathbf{i} + \sin\theta\sin\psi\,\mathbf{j} + \cos\theta\,\mathbf{k})\sin\theta\,d\theta d\psi,$$

where before integrating we express the cartesian components of $\mathbf{F}$ in terms of spherical polar coordinates on S by the relations

$$x = a\sin\theta\cos\psi, \qquad y = a\sin\theta\sin\psi, \qquad z = a\cos\theta. \qquad (3.47)$$

3.10   Solid Angle as a Surface Integral

In a plane, the angle subtended at a point O by an element AB of a given curve is equal to the arc length of the unit circle, centred at O,

E

contained between the lines OA, OB. As a generalization, in three dimensions we define the *magnitude of the solid angle* subtended at a point O by an area element dS of a surface to be the area of the unit sphere, centred at O, contained within the cone of lines from O to the boundary of dS (Fig. 3.14). In this definition, the units of solid angle are called *steradians*.

If a particular sense of direction for the unit normal $\hat{\mathbf{n}}$ is assigned to the element dS (e.g. the outward normal when dS is an element of a closed surface S) then the solid angle will be given a sign as well as magnitude, as follows. Let P be a point of dS with position vector $\mathbf{r}$ relative to O. The area intercepted by the cone of lines from O to the boundary of dS, on the sphere of radius r and centre O, is $dS \, | \, \hat{\mathbf{n}} . \hat{\mathbf{r}} \, |$, since $\hat{\mathbf{n}} . \hat{\mathbf{r}}$ is the cosine of the angle between $\hat{\mathbf{n}}$ and $\hat{\mathbf{r}}$. (In Fig. 3.14, $\hat{\mathbf{n}} . \hat{\mathbf{r}}$ is

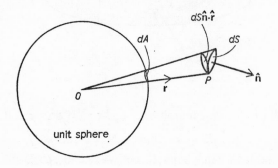

Fig. 3.14

positive, and the modulus sign is unnecessary in the case depicted.) By similar figures, we have that the area intercepted on the unit sphere by the cone is

$$dA = \frac{dS \, |\hat{\mathbf{n}} . \hat{\mathbf{r}}|}{r^2} = \frac{dS \, |\hat{\mathbf{n}} . \mathbf{r}|}{r^3}. \tag{3.48}$$

We *define* the solid angle subtended at O by the element dS with normal $\hat{\mathbf{n}}$ to be given in sign as well as magnitude by the expression

$$\frac{dS \, \hat{\mathbf{n}} . \mathbf{r}}{r^3}, \tag{3.49}$$

which is positive when $\hat{\mathbf{n}}$ makes an acute angle with $\mathbf{r}$ and negative when $\hat{\mathbf{n}}$ makes an obtuse angle with $\mathbf{r}$.

On integration, we have that the total solid angle subtended at O by an extended surface S is

$$\int_S \frac{\mathbf{r} . d\mathbf{S}}{r^3}, \tag{3.50}$$

where we have written $d\mathbf{S}$ to denote $\hat{\mathbf{n}} \, dS$.

Suppose that S is a closed surface, and that O is an interior point. Then it may be that some lines from O to S meet S in more than two points, as in Fig. 3.15. Consider the contributions to (3.50) from the three

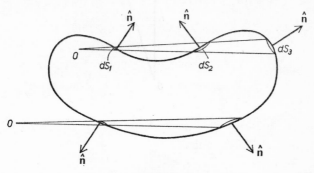

Fig. 3.15

intercepted elements. These are each equal in magnitude to the area of intersection dA of the elementary cone on the unit sphere with centre O. But the sign of the contributions from dS_1 and dS_3 are positive while that from dS_2 is negative, since in each case the sign is that of $\hat{\mathbf{n}} . \hat{\mathbf{r}}$, where $\mathbf{r}$ is the vector from O to the surface element in question. Thus, the contributions from dS_1 and dS_2 cancel, and so only the contribution from the outermost element need be counted. An elementary cone whose vertex is an interior point O will always meet a closed surface S in an odd number of intercepts, and the contributions from all but the outermost will cancel in pairs. In every such case, therefore, the value of the integral (3.50) is equal to 4π, the area of the unit sphere.

When O is an *exterior* point, the elementary cones meet the closed surface S in an even number of intercepts, and the contributions from these cancel in pairs. The total solid angle subtended by S at O is therefore zero.

Example. Find the solid angle subtended by a circle of radius a at a point on its axis of symmetry at distance h from the centre.

Method 1. Take plane polar coordinates R, ψ in the circle with centre Q as pole (Fig. 3.16).

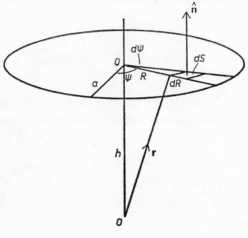

Fig. 3.16

Take $d\mathbf{S} = R\,dR\,d\psi\,\hat{\mathbf{n}}$, so that

$$\mathbf{r}.d\mathbf{S} = \mathbf{r}.\hat{\mathbf{n}}\,R\,dR\,d\psi = hR\,dR\,d\psi.$$

Therefore,

$$
\begin{aligned}
\int \frac{\mathbf{r}.d\mathbf{S}}{r^3} &= \int_0^a \int_0^{2\pi} \frac{hR\,dR\,d\psi}{(h^2+R^2)^{\frac{3}{2}}} \\
&= 2\pi h \int_0^a \frac{R\,dR}{(h^2+R^2)^{\frac{3}{2}}} \\
&= -2\pi h \left| (h^2+R^2)^{-\frac{1}{2}} \right|_0^a \\
&= 2\pi \left\{ 1 - \frac{h}{(h^2+a^2)^{\frac{1}{2}}} \right\}.
\end{aligned}
\tag{3.51}
$$

Method 2. Construct the sphere, with centre O, which passes through the circumference of the circle. Then the required solid angle, σ, is the same as that subtended by the spherical cap shown shaded in Fig. 3.17. Let the area of the cap be C. Since the solid angle subtended at the centre of a given sphere by a cap is proportional to the area of the cap,

$$\frac{\sigma}{4\pi} = \frac{C}{4\pi c^2},$$

where $c = (a^2+h^2)^{\frac{1}{2}}$ is the radius of the sphere. Here, we have used the result that 4π is the solid angle subtended at the centre by the whole sphere. But, by a theorem due to Archimedes,

$$\frac{C}{4\pi c^2} = \frac{QN}{MN} = \frac{c(1-\cos\theta)}{2c}$$

Therefore,

$$\sigma = \frac{C}{c^2} = 2\pi(1-\cos\theta) = 2\pi\left\{1 - \frac{h}{(h^2+a^2)^{\frac{1}{2}}}\right\},$$

as before.

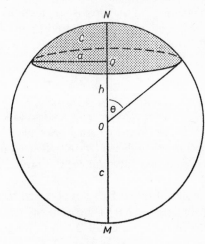

Fig. 3.17

3.11   Some Further Types of Surface Integral

Quantities such as

(a) $\int_S \mathbf{F} \wedge d\mathbf{S} = \int_S \mathbf{F} \wedge \hat{\mathbf{n}} \, dS;$ (b) $\int_S f \, d\mathbf{S} = \int_S f\hat{\mathbf{n}} \, dS,$

where $\mathbf{F}$ and f are vector and scalar functions defined at all points of a surface S, are meaningful. Each can be expressed as the limit of an appropriate sum. In (a), the integral is the vector whose component form is

$$\mathbf{i}\int_S (\mathbf{F} \wedge \hat{\mathbf{n}})_x \, dS + \mathbf{j}\int_S (\mathbf{F} \wedge \hat{\mathbf{n}})_y \, dS + \mathbf{k}\int_S (\mathbf{F} \wedge \hat{\mathbf{n}})_z \, dS$$

where each integrand is a scalar. The integral (b) is also a vector, its component form being

$$\mathbf{i} \int_S f\hat{n}_x \, dS + \mathbf{j} \int_S f\hat{n}_y \, dS + \mathbf{k} \int_S f\hat{n}_z \, dS,$$

where $\hat{\mathbf{n}} = \hat{n}_x \mathbf{i} + \hat{n}_y \mathbf{j} + \hat{n}_z \mathbf{k}$.

A simple physical example of (b) is the expression for the force due to pressure exerted by an *inviscid* (frictionless) fluid on a surface S immersed in the fluid and moving with it. It is a fundamental property of inviscid fluids that the force exerted on a surface element ΔS is directed normally towards the element. If the element is moving with the local velocity of the fluid, and the magnitude of the force is ΔF, then the limiting ratio of $\Delta F / \Delta S$ as the element is allowed to shrink to the point P is by definition the *pressure p* at P. Thus

$$p = \lim_{\Delta S \to 0} \frac{\Delta F}{\Delta S}.$$

It is implied in this definition that p is independent of the orientation of the element, and this fact is proved in books on fluid dynamics by considering the motion of an elementary tetrahedron of the fluid (with three mutually perpendicular faces) under the pressure and any other forces acting on it.

The force on one side of the surface S is obtained by summing all the approximate contributions $-p\hat{\mathbf{n}} \, \Delta S$ from elements ΔS, where $\hat{\mathbf{n}}$ is directed away from ΔS. In the limit, as all $\Delta S \to 0$, we get the integral of form (b) for the force,

$$- \int_S p\hat{\mathbf{n}} \, dS = - \int_S p \, d\mathbf{S}. \tag{3.52}$$

In particular, (3.52) is the resultant force on a *closed* surface S, due to pressure, where $\hat{\mathbf{n}}$ is the outward drawn normal.

Exercise. Consider a fluid at rest in which the pressure is uniform. By considering the equilibrium of a region of the fluid bounded by S, deduce that for any closed surface S,

$$\int_S d\mathbf{S} = 0.$$

Prove this result, also, mathematically by considering the projection of each element $d\mathbf{S}$ on each of the planes $x = 0$, $y = 0$, $z = 0$.

3.12   Volume Integrals

Let V denote a region of space which is divided in any manner into n elements of volume ΔV_r, $(r = 1, 2, \ldots, n)$ and let $f(x, y, z)$ be a scalar function defined at all points of V. Denote by f_r the value of f at any chosen point $P_r(x_r, y_r, z_r)$ in ΔV_r. If the sum

$$\sum_{r=1}^{n} f_r \, \Delta V_r$$

tends to a definite limit as the dimensions of all the ΔV_r tend to zero (and n tends to infinity), the limit being independent of the manner of subdivision and the particular point P_r chosen in ΔV_r, then we write

$$\int_V f \, dV = \lim_{\Delta V_r \to 0} \sum_{r=1}^{n} f_r \, \Delta V_r \tag{3.53}$$

and call this quantity the *volume integral* of f over V. By choosing each ΔV to be a rectangular element with sides $\Delta x \, \Delta y \, \Delta z$ parallel to the coordinate axes, we see that the integral may be evaluated as an ordinary triple integral

$$\iiint f(x, y, z) \, dx \, dy \, dz,$$

where the limits of integration are determined by the boundary of V. To emphasize that (3.53) normally involves triple integration, one sometimes writes the left hand side using three integral signs,

$$\iiint_V f \, dV.$$

We *define* the volume integral of a vector function $\mathbf{F}(x, y, z)$ (defined throughout V) as the vector

$$\int_V \mathbf{F} \, dV = \mathbf{i} \int_V F_x \, dV + \mathbf{j} \int_V F_y \, dV + \mathbf{k} \int_V F_z \, dV, \tag{3.54}$$

where $\mathbf{F} = F_x \mathbf{i} + F_y \mathbf{j} + F_z \mathbf{k}$.

Volume integrals of scalars and vectors over bounded regions ordinarily exist when the scalars and vectors are continuous everywhere in the regions.

As a physical example of (3.54), consider the momentum of a fluid in motion. At any instant, let the mass density (i.e. mass per unit volume) at any point $P(x, y, z)$ be $\rho(x, y, z)$ and let the local velocity be $\mathbf{q}(x, y, z)$. Then the momentum of the fluid in an element of volume ΔV containing

P is approximately $\rho\mathbf{q}\,\Delta V$, since $\rho\,\Delta V$ is approximately the mass of the element. On summing over all elements and taking the limit as all ΔV tend to zero, we obtain for the total momentum of the fluid instantaneously occupying a volume V, the integral $\int_V \rho\mathbf{q}\,dV$, which is of the form (3.54).

EXERCISES

1.   Evaluate $\int \mathbf{F}.d\mathbf{r}$, where $\mathbf{F} = xz\mathbf{i}+y\mathbf{j}-x^2\mathbf{k}$, along the curve $x = \sin\theta\cos\theta$, $y = \sin^2\theta$, $z = \cos\theta$, with θ increasing from 0 to $\frac{1}{2}\pi$.

2.   Calculate $\int_A^B yze^{x^2z}\,dx$ along the curve $z=x^2$, $y = x$, where A is the point $(-1, -1, 1)$ and B the point $(2, 2, 4)$.

3.   Sketch the curve C: $x = a\cos t$, $y = 2a\sin t$, $z = at$, where a is a positive constant and t increases along C from 0 to π.

    A force $\mathbf{F}$ acting on a particle P is given by $\mathbf{F} = xy\mathbf{i}-x^2\mathbf{j}+zx\mathbf{k}$, when the position of P is any point (x, y, z). Find the work done by $\mathbf{F}$ if P moves along the curve C.

4.   If $\mathbf{F} = 2xy^2\mathbf{i}+2x^2y\mathbf{j}-3z^3\mathbf{k}$, evaluate $\int_O^C \mathbf{F}.d\mathbf{r}$ along the path $OABC$ formed by straight line segments, where O is the origin and A, B, C are the points $(1, 0, 0)$, $(1, 2, 0)$, $(1, 2, 2)$ respectively. Verify the result by finding a function $f(x, y, z)$ such that

$$\mathbf{F} = \frac{\partial f}{\partial x}\mathbf{i}+\frac{\partial f}{\partial y}\mathbf{j}+\frac{\partial f}{\partial z}\mathbf{k}$$

and using the method described on page 49.

5.   If $\phi = xyz^2$, evaluate $\int_\Gamma \phi\,d\mathbf{r}$, where (i) Γ is the curve $x = t$, $y = t^2$, $z = t^3$ with t increasing from 0 to 1, (ii) Γ is the curve $OABC$ in exercise 4.

6.   When an electric current I flows along a wire placed in a magnetic field, a mechanical force acts on the wire. Given that the force acting on an element $d\mathbf{r}$ (directed in the sense of the current flow) is

$$d\mathbf{F} = I\,d\mathbf{r}\wedge\mathbf{B},$$

where $\mathbf{B}$ is the *magnetic induction* (in S.I. or rationalized m.k.s. units), prove that the total moment about O of the force acting on a closed loop C is

$$\mathbf{M} = I\int_C \mathbf{r}\wedge(d\mathbf{r}\wedge\mathbf{B}),$$

where $\mathbf{r}$ is the position vector of the element $d\mathbf{r}$ relative to 0.

    If the loop is in the form of a circle of radius a in the xy plane and $\mathbf{B}$ is a constant vector which makes an angle θ with the z axis, prove that $\mathbf{M}$ has magnitude $\pi a^2 BI\sin\theta$ and is in a direction perpendicular to $\mathbf{B}$ in the xy plane. (Resolve $\mathbf{r}$, $d\mathbf{r}$ and $\mathbf{B}$ into rectangular components, taking the y axis so that $\mathbf{B}$ is in the yz plane.)

7.   Evaluate $\int \mathbf{r}.d\mathbf{S}$, where $\mathbf{r} = x\mathbf{i}+y\mathbf{j}+z\mathbf{k}$, over (i) the surface of the unit cube bounded by the planes $x = 0$, $x = 1$, $y = 0$, $y = 1$, $z = 0$, $z = 1$, and (ii) the surface of the sphere of radius a centred at the origin.

8. Calculate the normal surface integral of the vector $3xz^2\mathbf{i} - x\mathbf{j} - y\mathbf{k}$ over that part of the curved surface of the cylinder $y^2 + z^2 = 4$ for which $y \geqslant 0$, $z \geqslant 0, 0 \leqslant x \leqslant 3$.

9. In an electromagnetic field, the rate of flow of electromagnetic energy out through a closed surface S is equal to the flux of $\mathbf{E} \wedge \mathbf{H}$ through S, where $\mathbf{E}$ is the electric field vector and $\mathbf{H}$ the magnetic field vector. If $\mathbf{E} = E_0 \sin k(z - ct)\mathbf{i}$, $\mathbf{H} = H_0 \sin k(z - ct)\mathbf{j}$, where E_0, H_0 and k are constants, show that the rate of energy flow out through the surface of the cube bounded by the planes $x = 0$, $x = a, y = 0, y = a, z = 0, z = a$ is

$$E_0 H_0 a^2 \sin ka \sin k(a - 2ct).$$

10. Sketch the surface S: $z = 1 - x^2 - y^2$. Calculate the flux of the vector $\mathbf{r} = x\mathbf{i} + y\mathbf{j} + z\mathbf{k}$ out through the closed surface formed by that part of S for which $z > 0$, together with the base $z = 0$, $x^2 + y^2 \leqslant 1$.

11. If $\mathbf{F}$ denotes the vector $(y - x)\mathbf{j} + (z - 2y)\mathbf{k}$, evaluate the surface integral $\int \mathbf{F} \wedge d\mathbf{S}$ over the open surface of the hemisphere $x^2 + y^2 + z^2 = a^2$, $x > 0$, where $d\mathbf{S}$ is directed away from the origin.

12. Sketch the surface S: $x = \sin u \cos v, y = \sin u \sin v, z = 2\cos u$, where $0 \leqslant u \leqslant \frac{1}{2}\pi, 0 \leqslant v \leqslant \frac{1}{2}\pi$. (Eliminate u and v first.) Calculate the unit tangent vectors along the coordinate lines $v = const.$ (u increasing) and $u = const.$ (v increasing), and obtain an expression for the line element of the surface.
    Determine also the area of S.

13. If $\mathbf{F} = xy\mathbf{i} - z\mathbf{j} + 2xz\mathbf{k}$, calculate $\int \mathbf{F} \, dV$ over (i) the rectangular region $0 \leqslant x \leqslant 1$, $0 \leqslant y \leqslant 1$, $0 \leqslant z \leqslant 2$, (ii) the cylindrical region $x^2 + y^2 \leqslant 4$, $0 \leqslant z \leqslant 3$, and (iii) the interior of the sphere $x^2 + y^2 + z^2 = 1$.
    (Hint: For (ii), take $dV = R \, dR d\psi dz$ in cylindrical polar coordinates, and for (iii), take $dV = r^2 \sin \theta \, dr d\theta d\psi$ in spherical polar coordinates. See Figs. 10.2, 10.3).

CHAPTER 4

The Gradient Vector

4.1 The Gradient of a Scalar Point Function

The expression

$$\nabla \equiv \mathbf{i}\frac{\partial}{\partial x} + \mathbf{j}\frac{\partial}{\partial y} + \mathbf{k}\frac{\partial}{\partial z} \qquad (4.1)$$

is an example of a *vector differential operator*, and is called *nabla* or *del*. It may act on a scalar or vector point function, but for the moment we shall consider only its action on a scalar. It is important in (4.1) that the vectors $\mathbf{i}$, $\mathbf{j}$ and $\mathbf{k}$ be written to the left of the partial differentiation operators, since, for example $(\partial/\partial x)\mathbf{i}$ is not the same as $\mathbf{i}\partial/\partial x$, the former being zero and the latter being an operator.

If $\phi(x, y, z)$ is any scalar point function possessing first partial derivatives with respect to x, y and z, then the vector

$$\operatorname{grad}\phi \equiv \nabla\phi = \mathbf{i}\frac{\partial\phi}{\partial x} + \mathbf{j}\frac{\partial\phi}{\partial y} + \mathbf{k}\frac{\partial\phi}{\partial z} \qquad (4.2)$$

is called the *gradient* of ϕ. The gradient is very important in applications, and we shall determine some of its properties in this chapter.

One is familiar, on maps, with the use of contour lines (lines of constant altitude) to show how the altitude changes over the surface of the mapped region. In 3-dimensional space, contour surfaces or *level surfaces* of a scalar ϕ are similarly useful. These are defined to be the family of surfaces

$$\phi(x, y, z) = \text{constant.} \qquad (4.3)$$

If we assume that ϕ is a single valued function in the region of interest, i.e. to each point (x, y, z) there is just one value of ϕ, then the level surfaces cannot intersect. For, if A is a point of intersection of two level surfaces $\phi = c_1$, $\phi = c_2$ $(c_1 \neq c_2)$, then ϕ has the two values c_1 and c_2 at A, which contradicts the assumption that it is single valued.

There is a level surface through every point $P(x_P, y_P, z_P)$ in the region, because the surface $\phi(x, y, z) = \phi(x_P, y_P, z_P)$ contains the point P. Consider the differential displacement vector $d\mathbf{r} = dx\,\mathbf{i} + dy\,\mathbf{j} + dz\,\mathbf{k}$ from any chosen point P to a neighbouring point Q in the region. The increment in ϕ in this displacement, $\phi_Q - \phi_P$, is approximately equal to the differential $d\phi$, where by the chain rule for differentials

$$d\phi = \frac{\partial \phi}{\partial x}dx + \frac{\partial \phi}{\partial y}dy + \frac{\partial \phi}{\partial z}dz. \tag{4.4}$$

By the definition (4.2), we can write this fundamental relation as

$$d\phi = (\text{grad}\,\phi)\,.\,d\mathbf{r}. \tag{4.5}$$

This is an exact relation between differentials, although we often use it in practice to remind us that $(\text{grad}\,\phi)\,.\,\Delta\mathbf{r}$ is approximately the increment $\Delta\phi$ in ϕ corresponding to a small displacement $\Delta\mathbf{r}$, terms of smaller order than $\Delta\mathbf{r}$ being neglected.

Suppose that Q is on the tangent plane at P to the level surface through P. Then $d\phi = 0$, and so (omitting the brackets)

$$\text{grad}\,\phi\,.\,d\mathbf{r} = 0, \tag{4.6}$$

which shows that $\text{grad}\,\phi$ is orthogonal to every displacement on the tangent plane and is therefore *in the direction of the normal to the level surface through* P.

The direction of the normal at P to the level surface of ϕ is also the direction in which ϕ is changing most rapidly with respect to displacements from P. For, letting Q now be any point on a definite neighbouring

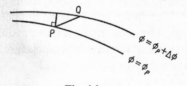

Fig. 4.1

level surface $\phi = \phi_P + \Delta\phi$, where $\phi = \phi_P$ is the equation of the level surface through P, and $\Delta\phi$ is constant, then whatever particular point is chosen for Q, the same increment $\Delta\phi$ is obtained on making a displacement from P to Q. This increment occurs with smallest displacement when PQ is orthogonal to the surface $\phi = \phi_P$ (Fig. 4.1), and the result follows. (Remember that neighbouring level surfaces are nearly parallel because they cannot intersect.)

To determine the magnitude of grad ϕ at P, we next let Q be on the normal to the level surface $\phi = \phi_P$, with $\overrightarrow{PQ}$ having the same sense of direction as grad ϕ. Write $\overrightarrow{PQ} = \hat{\mathbf{n}}\,dl$, where $\hat{\mathbf{n}}$ is the unit normal vector at P and dl denotes PQ. Then, by (4.5)

$$d\phi = \operatorname{grad}\phi\,.\,\hat{\mathbf{n}}\,dl = |\operatorname{grad}\phi|\,dl, \qquad (4.7)$$

because $\hat{\mathbf{n}}$ is a *unit* vector and is parallel to grad ϕ. Thus, the magnitude of grad ϕ is equal to the rate of increase of ϕ in the direction $\overrightarrow{PQ}$,

$$|\operatorname{grad}\phi| = \frac{d\phi}{dl}. \qquad (4.8)$$

We note from (4.8) that ϕ is *increasing* in the direction of grad ϕ, because $d\phi/dl$ is positive. The properties of the gradient of a scalar function may therefore be summarized as follows:

grad ϕ *is a vector whose direction is that of the greatest rate of increase of ϕ, with respect to displacement, and whose magnitude is equal to that rate of increase.*

The rate of change of a scalar ϕ in the direction of the normal $\mathbf{n}$ to a given surface is often denoted by $\partial\phi/\partial n$, in which case (4.8) would be written

$$|\operatorname{grad}\phi| = \frac{\partial\phi}{\partial n}. \qquad (4.9)$$

Example. The temperature in a region of space is $cy^2(x-z)$, where c is a positive constant. If an insect sets off from the point $(1, 1, 2)$ with given speed v, in an attempt to get warm as fast as possible, in which direction should it fly? What rate of increase of temperature, with respect to time, will it meet if it chooses the right direction?

Let ϕ denote $cy^2(x-z)$. Then

$$\begin{aligned}
\operatorname{grad}\phi &= \mathbf{i}\frac{\partial\phi}{\partial x}+\mathbf{j}\frac{\partial\phi}{\partial y}+\mathbf{k}\frac{\partial\phi}{\partial z} \\
&= c(y^2\mathbf{i}+2y(x-z)\mathbf{j}-y^2\mathbf{k}) \\
&= c(\mathbf{i}-2\mathbf{j}-\mathbf{k})
\end{aligned}$$

at the point $(1, 1, 2)$. Therefore, the required direction is that of the vector $\mathbf{i}-2\mathbf{j}-\mathbf{k}$.

The spatial rate of increase of ϕ in this direction at the point $(1, 1, 2)$ is

$$\frac{d\phi}{dl} = |\text{grad } \phi| = c\sqrt{6}.$$

Therefore, the time rate of increase of temperature encountered by the insect if it flies in this direction is

$$\frac{d\phi}{dt} = \frac{d\phi}{dl}\frac{dl}{dt} = (c\sqrt{6})v = \sqrt{6}cv.$$

4.2 Invariance of the Gradient

In (4.2), it is not immediately evident that the vector so defined is independent of the orientation and origin of the coordinate axes. If a different set of rectangular cartesian axes $O'x'y'z'$ were chosen instead of $Oxyz$, with unit vectors $\mathbf{i}', \mathbf{j}', \mathbf{k}'$ in the x', y', z' directions respectively, would the vector

$$\mathbf{i}'\frac{\partial\phi'}{\partial x'} + \mathbf{j}'\frac{\partial\phi'}{\partial y'} + \mathbf{k}'\frac{\partial\phi'}{\partial z'} \tag{4.10}$$

have the same magnitude and direction in space as (4.2)? Here, it is assumed that ϕ has a definite value at each point of space, whether the point is labelled (x, y, z) or (x', y', z'), and $\phi'(x', y', z')$ denotes the expression for ϕ at such a point in terms of primed coordinates, so that $\phi'(x', y', z') = \phi(x, y, z)$. (We say that ϕ is an *invariant* under the *transformation of coordinates*.)

To be of physical value, the definition of the gradient of a scalar should not depend on a particular choice of rectangular coordinate system. The fact that the gradient can be identified in magnitude and direction with the greatest rate of change of the scalar concerned proves that the definition is indeed independent of the choice of axes. The gradient of an invariant scalar function is itself *invariant* under the transformation of coordinates.

4.3 Directional Derivatives

The gradient vector may be used to calculate the rate of change of a scalar function, at a point P, in *any* given direction. Let $\hat{\mathbf{a}}$ be a *unit* vector in the given direction, and let dl be the magnitude of a displacement from

P. The differential of the scalar ϕ corresponding to this displacement is

$$d\phi = \operatorname{grad}\phi . \hat{a}\,dl,$$

and so for the required rate of change we have

$$\frac{d\phi}{dl} = \hat{a}.\operatorname{grad}\phi. \qquad (4.11)$$

This is called the *directional derivative* of ϕ in the direction $\hat{a}$. It is important that $\hat{a}$ be a *unit* vector in (4.11). Note also that the directional derivative is simply the resolved component of $\operatorname{grad}\phi$ in the direction $\hat{a}$.

Sometimes, the unfortunate notation $\partial\phi/\partial\hat{a}$ is used for the directional derivative in the direction $\hat{a}$.

Example. Find the rate of change of the function $x^3 + y^2z$, with respect to distance, at the point $P(2, 1, 1)$: (i) in the direction of x increasing, (ii) in the direction of the point $(1, 1, -3)$ from P.

Let ϕ denote $x^3 + y^2z$. Then

$$\operatorname{grad}\phi = 3x^2\mathbf{i} + 2yz\mathbf{j} + y^2\mathbf{k}$$

$$= 12\mathbf{i} + 2\mathbf{j} + \mathbf{k}$$

at the point $(2, 1, 1)$. For (i), we have that $\mathbf{i}$ is the unit vector in the direction of x increasing, and so the required rate of change is

$$\mathbf{i}.\operatorname{grad}\phi = 12.$$

For (ii), the vector displacement from the point $(2, 1, 1)$ to the point $(1, 1-3)$ is $-\mathbf{i} - 4\mathbf{k}$, and the *unit* vector in this direction is

$$\hat{a} = \frac{1}{\sqrt{17}}(-\mathbf{i} - 4\mathbf{k}).$$

Therefore, the required directional derivative is

$$\hat{a}.\operatorname{grad}\phi = \frac{1}{\sqrt{17}}(-12-4) = -\frac{16}{\sqrt{17}}.$$

4.4   Some Differentiation Formulae

In the following, a and b are constants, $u(x, y, z)$ and $v(x, y, z)$ are differentiable scalar point functions and $\phi(u)$ is a differentiable function of u:

$$\text{grad}\,(au+bv) = a\,\text{grad}\,u + b\,\text{grad}\,v, \tag{4.12}$$

$$\text{grad}\,(uv) = u\,\text{grad}\,v + v\,\text{grad}\,u, \tag{4.13}$$

$$\text{grad}\,\phi(u) = \frac{d\phi}{du}\text{grad}\,u. \tag{4.14}$$

These identities are proved using the definition (4.2) and standard formulae of elementary calculus. The proof of (4.12) is trivial and is left to the reader. To prove (4.13), we have

$$\begin{aligned}
\text{grad}\,(uv) &= \mathbf{i}\frac{\partial}{\partial x}(uv) + \mathbf{j}\frac{\partial}{\partial y}(uv) + \mathbf{k}\frac{\partial}{\partial z}(uv) \\
&= \mathbf{i}\left(u\frac{\partial v}{\partial x} + v\frac{\partial u}{\partial x}\right) + \mathbf{j}\left(u\frac{\partial v}{\partial y} + v\frac{\partial u}{\partial y}\right) + \mathbf{k}\left(u\frac{\partial v}{\partial z} + v\frac{\partial u}{\partial z}\right) \\
&= u\left(\mathbf{i}\frac{\partial v}{\partial x} + \mathbf{j}\frac{\partial v}{\partial y} + \mathbf{k}\frac{\partial v}{\partial z}\right) + v\left(\mathbf{i}\frac{\partial u}{\partial x} + \mathbf{j}\frac{\partial u}{\partial y} + \mathbf{k}\frac{\partial u}{\partial z}\right) \\
&= u\,\text{grad}\,v + v\,\text{grad}\,u.
\end{aligned}$$

To prove (4.14), which is the 'function of a function rule' for gradient differentiation, we have

$$\begin{aligned}
\text{grad}\,\phi(u) &= \mathbf{i}\frac{\partial}{\partial x}\phi(u) + \mathbf{j}\frac{\partial}{\partial y}\phi(u) + \mathbf{k}\frac{\partial}{\partial z}\phi(u) \\
&= \mathbf{i}\frac{d\phi}{du}\frac{\partial u}{\partial x} + \mathbf{j}\frac{d\phi}{du}\frac{\partial u}{\partial y} + \mathbf{k}\frac{d\phi}{du}\frac{\partial u}{\partial z} \\
&= \frac{d\phi}{du}\left(\mathbf{i}\frac{\partial u}{\partial x} + \mathbf{j}\frac{\partial u}{\partial y} + \mathbf{k}\frac{\partial u}{\partial z}\right) \\
&= \frac{d\phi}{du}\text{grad}\,u.
\end{aligned}$$

When a differentiation operator L, which can act on scalar functions, is such that

$$L(au+bv) = aL(u) + bL(v),$$

where a and b are any constants and u and v are scalar functions with appropriate continuity and differentiability properties, it is called a *linear differential operator*. Thus, by (4.12), the gradient operator is linear. Other linear differential operators are, for example,

$$z\frac{\partial}{\partial x}, \quad \frac{\partial^2}{\partial y^2}, \quad 2\mathbf{i}\frac{\partial}{\partial x} + \mathbf{j}\frac{\partial^2}{\partial z^2}, \quad \text{etc.}$$

Example. Evaluate $\operatorname{grad} r^n$, where n is a constant and $r = (x^2+y^2+z^2)^{\frac{1}{2}}$ is the distance from the origin to a general point (x, y, z).

We have

$$\operatorname{grad} r^n = \operatorname{grad}(x^2+y^2+z^2)^{n/2}$$

$$= \frac{n}{2}(x^2+y^2+z^2)^{n/2-1}\operatorname{grad}(x^2+y^2+z^2), \quad \text{by (4.14)},$$

$$= \frac{n}{2}r^{n-2}(2x\mathbf{i}+2y\mathbf{j}+2z\mathbf{k})$$

$$= nr^{n-2}\mathbf{r} = nr^{n-1}\hat{\mathbf{r}}, \tag{4.15}$$

where $\mathbf{r} = \overrightarrow{OP}$ is the vector from the origin to the field point $P(x, y, z)$ at which the calculation is made.

Alternatively, we may say that the level surfaces of the function r^n are the spheres $r = \text{const.}$ For positive n, the direction of greatest increase of r^n is that of the vector $\hat{\mathbf{r}}$, and the magnitude of $\operatorname{grad} r^n$ is therefore the rate at which r^n increases with r, i.e.

$$\frac{d}{dr}r^n = nr^{n-1},$$

which agrees with (4.15). For negative n, the direction of $\operatorname{grad} r^n$ is $-\hat{\mathbf{r}}$, and its magnitude is therefore

$$-\frac{d}{dr}r^n = -nr^{n-1}.$$

This again gives the formula (4.15). Finally, the case $n = 0$ is trivial, since both sides of (4.15) are clearly zero.

Note the special case $n = 1$ in the above example, i.e.

$$\operatorname{grad} r = \hat{\mathbf{r}}. \tag{4.16}$$

Using this, and the rule (4.14) with $u \equiv r$, we have for any differentiable function $f(r)$

$$\operatorname{grad} f(r) = \frac{df}{dr}\hat{\mathbf{r}}. \tag{4.17}$$

4.5   Tangential Line Integration as the Inverse to Gradient Differentiation

Just as in one-variable calculus integration is the inverse operation to differentiation, so is tangential line integration, in a certain sense, the inverse operation to gradient differentiation. This result is bound up in the following important theorem.

Theorem. A necessary and sufficient condition for the tangential line integral (T.L.I.) of a continuous vector function $\mathbf{F}$

$$\int_A^B \mathbf{F} . d\mathbf{r}$$

to depend only on the points A and B, *and not on the path of integration from A to B,* in a given region R is that $\mathbf{F}$ be the gradient of a single valued scalar function everywhere in R.

Proof: Sufficience. This is simple, and the result has already been met (p. 48). Suppose that there exists a single valued scalar $\phi(x, y, z)$ such that $\mathbf{F} = \operatorname{grad}\phi$ everywhere in R. Then for any path C joining A and B we have

$$\int_{\substack{A\\C}}^B \mathbf{F} . d\mathbf{r} = \int_{\substack{A\\C}}^B \operatorname{grad}\phi . d\mathbf{r} = \int_{\substack{A\\C}}^B d\phi = \left.\left|\phi\right|\right._A^B$$

$$= \phi(x_B, y_B, z_B) - \phi(x_A, y_A, z_A), \tag{4.18}$$

where (x_A, y_A, z_A) and (x_B, y_B, z_B) are the coordinates of the points A and B respectively. This shows explicitly the dependence of the T.L.I. on the end points of the path of integration only.

Note that if $P(x, y, z)$ is a general point in R, then by (4.18), with P replacing B,

$$\phi(x, y, z) = \int_A^P \mathbf{F} . d\mathbf{r} + \phi(x_A, y_A, z_A)$$

$$= \int_A^P \operatorname{grad}\phi . d\mathbf{r} + \phi(x_A, y_A, z_A), \tag{4.19}$$

where the path of integration is immaterial. Thus, apart from a constant, the T.L.I. of the gradient of ϕ is equal to ϕ, which shows that tangential line integration is the inverse operation to forming the gradient.

Necessity. Let a definite point A be chosen as initial point on the path of integration and, as before, let $P(x, y, z)$ be a general point in R. By hypothesis, the scalar function

$$\psi(x, y, z) = \int_A^P \mathbf{F} . d\mathbf{r} \tag{4.20}$$

is single valued, because its value at (x, y, z) does not depend on the path of integration. We shall prove that the gradient of ψ is equal to $\mathbf{F}$.

The right hand side of (4.20) can be written

$$\int \mathbf{F} . \hat{\mathbf{t}} \, ds \tag{4.21}$$

where $\hat{\mathbf{t}}$ is the unit tangent vector to the path at a general point and s

F

denotes arc length measured from A. The lower limit in (4.21) is zero and the upper limit is the arc length AP. Now, suppose that any particular path of integration is extended a short distance in the direction of its tangent vector at P. Then, by differentiation with respect to s at P we get from (4.20), (4.21)

$$\frac{d\psi}{ds} = \mathbf{F} \cdot \hat{\mathbf{t}}, \text{ (evaluated at } P). \tag{4.22}$$

But, by the formula $d\psi = \operatorname{grad}\psi \cdot d\mathbf{r}$, with $d\mathbf{r} = \hat{\mathbf{t}}\,ds$, we have

$$\frac{d\psi}{ds} = \operatorname{grad}\psi \cdot \hat{\mathbf{t}}, \tag{4.23}$$

so that on subtraction

$$(\mathbf{F} - \operatorname{grad}\psi) \cdot \hat{\mathbf{t}} = 0$$

at $P(x, y, z)$.

By choice of the path, $\hat{\mathbf{t}}$ may have any direction at P, and so the vector $\mathbf{F} - \operatorname{grad}\psi$ must be orthogonal to *every* direction. This is possible only if

$$\mathbf{F} = \operatorname{grad}\psi, \tag{4.24}$$

which proves that the stated condition is necessary. Equations (4.24) and (4.20) show that the gradient of the T.L.I. of a vector is equal to the vector, which result is complementary to that quoted in the first part of the proof.

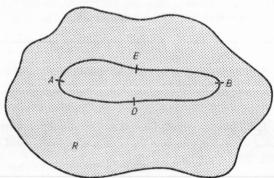

Fig. 4.2

An equivalent way of expressing that the T.L.I. of a particular vector $\mathbf{F}$ is independent of the path joining any two given points in a region R is the statement that the T.L.I. around every closed path in R is equal to zero. In Fig. 4.2, if A and B are any two points and ADB, AEB any two paths joining them, then we are given that

$$\int_{ADB} \mathbf{F} \cdot d\mathbf{r} = \int_{AEB} \mathbf{F} \cdot d\mathbf{r} = - \int_{BEA} \mathbf{F} \cdot d\mathbf{r}. \qquad (4.25)$$

Therefore the T.L.I. around the closed path $ADBEA$ is

$$\left(\int_{ADB} + \int_{BEA} \right) \mathbf{F} \cdot d\mathbf{r} = 0.$$

Every closed curve in R may be treated in this way by choosing as A and B any two points on it. Conversely, if the T.L.I. around every closed path in R is zero, then the T.L.I.'s along any two paths between the same pair of points are equal. This follows by reversing the previous argument.

4.6   Conservative Vector Fields

A field vector $\mathbf{F}$ is said to be *conservative* in a region when it is expressible throughout the region as the gradient of a single valued scalar function. The scalar ϕ such that

$$\mathbf{F} = -\operatorname{grad} \phi \qquad (4.26)$$

is called the *scalar potential* of the field. (Sometimes the positive sign is used in place of the negative sign in (4.26), especially in gravitation theory.) This equation defines ϕ only to within an arbitrary additive constant, for if $\phi_1(x, y, z)$ and $\phi_2(x, y, z)$ are two solutions for ϕ of (4.26), it does not follow that $\phi_1 \equiv \phi_2$, but only that $\operatorname{grad} \phi_1 \equiv \operatorname{grad} \phi_2$, i.e. that

$$\operatorname{grad} (\phi_1 - \phi_2) \equiv 0. \qquad (4.27)$$

Thus, all the partial derivatives of $\phi_1 - \phi_2$ are identically zero, which implies simply that $\phi_1 - \phi_2$ is a constant, not necessarily zero. In applications, the arbitrary constant in ϕ is unimportant, because one is always concerned with the difference in potential between two points of the region, so that the constant cancels.

By the results of the last theorem, we may take the explicit expression for ϕ at any point P

$$\phi(P) = - \int_A^P \mathbf{F} \cdot d\mathbf{r} \qquad (4.28)$$

where A and the path AP are arbitrary. The freedom in the choice of A corresponds to the arbitrary additive constant in ϕ.

As an example, suppose that the conservative vector $\mathbf{F}$ denotes a mechanical force acting on a mass particle. Then the work done by the force as the particle moves from an arbitrary initial 'base' point P_0 to a general point P along any path is

$$\int_{P_0}^{P} \mathbf{F} \cdot d\mathbf{r} = \int_{A}^{P} \mathbf{F} \cdot d\mathbf{r} - \int_{A}^{P_0} \mathbf{F} \cdot d\mathbf{r}$$
$$= \phi(P_0) - \phi(P),$$

which is the decrease in potential between the two points. The potential of the force field is therefore the same as the potential energy, familiar in elementary mechanics. Other examples of potential will be met later in this book.

EXERCISES

In the following, $\mathbf{r}$ denotes the vector $x\mathbf{i} + y\mathbf{j} + z\mathbf{k}$.

1. Find ∇xyz^2 at the point $(2, 3, 1)$.

2. Determine the directional derivative of the function xyz^2 in the direction of the vector $2\mathbf{i} + \mathbf{j} - \mathbf{k}$ at the point $(2, 3, 1)$.

3. Find ∇f, where (i) $f = xr$, (ii) $f = \sin r$, (iii) $f = e^{\sin r}$.

4. The atmospheric pressure in a certain region of space is $p = a(xy^2 + yz^2 + xyz)$ where a is a constant. Find the rate of change of pressure with respect to distance at the point $(1, 1, 4)$ in the region, in the direction of the vector $\mathbf{j} - 3\mathbf{k}$.

5. If $\mathbf{a}$ is a constant vector, show that $\nabla(\mathbf{a} \cdot \mathbf{r}) = \mathbf{a}$. Hence show that if $\mathbf{b}$ is also a constant vector, then

$$\nabla\{(\mathbf{a} \cdot \mathbf{r})(\mathbf{b} \cdot \mathbf{r})\} = (\mathbf{a} \cdot \mathbf{r})\mathbf{b} + (\mathbf{b} \cdot \mathbf{r})\mathbf{a}.$$

6. Prove that if $f(r)$ is a continuous single valued function, then

$$\oint f(r)\mathbf{r} \cdot d\mathbf{r} = 0$$

around any closed curve. (Hint: Is there a scalar function $F(r)$ such that $\nabla F = f(r)\mathbf{r}$ for every choice of f?)

7. If $\mathbf{F} = e^x z^{-2}\{yz(1 + x)\mathbf{i} + z(x + ze^{-x})\mathbf{j} - xy\mathbf{k}\}$, find a scalar function ϕ such that $\mathbf{F} = \operatorname{grad} \phi$.

8. The vacuum magnetic field $\mathbf{H}$ of a magnetic dipole of moment $\mathbf{M}$ placed at the origin is given by the formula $\mathbf{H} = -\nabla\Omega$, where $\Omega = -(1/4\pi)\mathbf{M} \cdot \nabla(1/r)$, in S.I. units. Prove that

$$\mathbf{H} = \frac{1}{4\pi}\left\{\frac{3(\mathbf{M} \cdot \mathbf{r})\mathbf{r}}{r^5} - \frac{\mathbf{M}}{r^3}\right\}$$

(Write $\mathbf{H} = -(1/4\pi)\nabla(r^{-3}\mathbf{M} \cdot \mathbf{r})$, and use (4.13) and the first formula in exercise 5.)

9. If $\mathbf{F}$ is a vector point function defined at all points of the surface S, whose equation is $\phi(x, y, z) = const.$, show that the vector component of $\mathbf{F}$ in the direction normal to S is

$$\frac{(\mathbf{F} \cdot \nabla\phi)\nabla\phi}{(\nabla\phi)^2}.$$

Find a corresponding expression for the tangential vector component of $\mathbf{F}$.

10. Find the equation of the tangent plane to the surface $zy^2 = (x+y)^3$ at the point $(1, 1, 8)$ on it.

11. If u and v are single valued, continuously differentiable point functions in a given region R, and C is any closed curve in R, show that

$$\text{(i)} \quad \oint_C u\nabla v \cdot d\mathbf{r} = -\oint_C v\nabla u \cdot d\mathbf{r},$$

$$\text{(ii)} \quad \oint_C \frac{\partial f}{\partial u}\nabla u \cdot d\mathbf{r} = -\oint_C \frac{\partial f}{\partial v}\nabla v \cdot d\mathbf{r}$$

where f is any single valued, continuously differentiable function of u and v.

CHAPTER 5

Electrostatic Applications

5.1 Electrostatic Fields and Potentials

We assume in this chapter that the reader is familiar with the elementary properties of electric charges. According to *Coulomb's experimental law*, two electric point charges e_1, e_2 at rest *in vacuo* attract or repel each other (according as the two charges are of unlike or like sign) with a mutual force whose magnitude is proportional to the product of the charges and inversely proportional to the square of the distance between them. Mathematically, the force on e_2 due to the presence of e_1 is expressed as

$$\mathbf{F}_2 = k\frac{e_1 e_2}{r^2}\hat{\mathbf{r}}_{12}, \tag{5.1}$$

where $\mathbf{r}_{12}$ is the vector displacement from the charge e_1 to the charge e_2, and k is a positive constant whose value depends on the choice of units. Two systems of units deserve mention.

The *electrostatic unit* (e.s.u.) of charge (in terms of centimetre-gramme-second units of length, mass and time) is defined by the requirement that equal point charges of 1 e.s.u. placed at a distance 1 centimetre apart exert a mutual force of 1 dyne. Thus, in e.s.u., $k = 1$ in (5.1). This system is becoming universally replaced by S.I. (Système International) units, incorporating the rationalized m.k.s. (metre-kilogramme-second) system in which force is measured in *newtons*, charge is measured in *coulombs*, and k has the value

$$k = \frac{1}{4\pi\varepsilon_0}. \tag{5.2}$$

Here, ε_0 is a certain constant (not a pure number) called the *permittivity of free space*, which arises in the later development of electromagnetic theory.

When a number, or *system*, of electric charges in vacuo are situated at different points, the resultant force that they would exert on a unit test charge placed at any point P is called the *electrostatic field* at P due to the system, and is denoted by the vector $\mathbf{E}$. Thus, the electrostatic field at the point $P(\mathbf{r})$ due to a point charge e at the origin is, by (5.1),

$$\mathbf{E}(\mathbf{r}) = \frac{e}{r^2}\hat{\mathbf{r}}, \qquad \text{(e.s.u. units)}, \tag{5.3}$$

$$\mathbf{E}(\mathbf{r}) = \frac{e}{4\pi\varepsilon_0 r^2}\hat{\mathbf{r}}, \qquad \text{(S.I. or m.k.s. units)}. \tag{5.4}$$

The field at $P(\mathbf{r})$ due to a more general system of, say, n point charges $e_1, e_2, \ldots, e_n$ situated respectively at the points with position vectors $\mathbf{r}_1, \mathbf{r}_2, \ldots, \mathbf{r}_n$ may be calculated using the *principle of superposition*. According to this principle, the field at P due to the system is the vector sum of the fields due to each charge alone. Therefore, in S.I. or m.k.s. units (which we shall henceforth use)

$$\mathbf{E}(\mathbf{r}) = \frac{1}{4\pi\varepsilon_0} \sum_{i=1}^{n} \frac{e_i}{|\mathbf{r}-\mathbf{r}_i|^3}(\mathbf{r}-\mathbf{r}_i), \tag{5.5}$$

(Fig. 5.1).

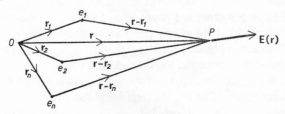

Fig. 5.1

The electrostatic field (5.4) is conservative, since if we define

$$\phi = \frac{e}{4\pi\varepsilon_0 r}, \tag{5.6}$$

then on forming the gradient we get, using (4.17),

$$-\operatorname{grad}\phi = -\frac{e}{4\pi\varepsilon_0}\operatorname{grad}\frac{1}{r} = \frac{e\hat{\mathbf{r}}}{4\pi\varepsilon_0 r^2} = \mathbf{E}.$$

The *electrostatic scalar potential* $e/4\pi\varepsilon_0 r$ due to a single point charge e at the origin is uniquely determined by the equation $\mathbf{E} = -\operatorname{grad}\phi$ together with the choice $\phi = 0$ at $r = \infty$, which is conventional. For the above system of charges, the contribution to the potential at $P(\mathbf{r})$ due to each individual charge e_i at the point $\mathbf{r}_i$ is

$$\phi_i = \frac{e_i}{4\pi\varepsilon_0|\mathbf{r}-\mathbf{r}_i|}. \tag{5.7}$$

Since the gradient operator is linear, the sum of the gradients of a number of functions is equal to the gradient of the sum of the functions, and so for the system with field (5.5) we have

$$\mathbf{E}(\mathbf{r}) = \sum_{i=1}^{n} (-\operatorname{grad}\phi_i) = -\operatorname{grad}(\sum_{i=1}^{n}\phi_i) = -\operatorname{grad}\phi, \tag{5.8}$$

where

$$\phi \equiv \sum_{i=1}^{n}\phi_i = \frac{1}{4\pi\varepsilon_0}\sum_{i=1}^{n}\frac{e_i}{|\mathbf{r}-\mathbf{r}_i|}. \tag{5.9}$$

This shows, by construction of the potential, that the vacuum electrostatic field of any finite number of electric point charges is conservative.

The reason for introducing the potential is this. When the position of every charge in a system is known, it is a straightforward matter to calculate the electric field at any point using (5.5). However, it is not normally the case in physical problems that the distribution of charge is known *a priori*. For example, the *total* electric charge on a certain conducting body might be known, together with other data which is sufficient to make the problem of finding the electric field at all points determinate, but this other data need not include an explicit statement of the way the charge is distributed on the conductor. Indeed, the fundamental property of a (perfect) conductor is that any electric charge on it will always distribute itself so as to make the *internal* electric field vanish, and this only tells us the distribution in an indirect way. The method of tackling such problems is as follows. By using vector analysis we can obtain a partial differential equation satisfied by all electrostatic field vectors *in vacuo* or in the presence of charge. (This is done in Chapter 6; see p.109.) The problem then is to solve this *field equation*, singling out the particular solution which is compatible with all the given data. Because it is naturally easier to work with an unknown scalar rather than an unknown vector, it is usually preferable to replace the partial differential equation for $\mathbf{E}$ by an equivalent one for the potential ϕ. The electric field $\mathbf{E}$ can be found at the end of a calculation by forming (minus) the gradient of ϕ.

5.2   Continuous Distributions of Charge

When a sufficiently large number of electric charges are distributed within a given volume region V, it may be convenient for practical purposes to regard the distribution as *continuous*. This means that we approximate the distribution by an ideal one in which the charge is spread out smoothly in the region. Let Δe be the charge contained within an element $\Delta V'$ containing the point $Q(x', y', z')$. Then the *volume density* of charge at Q is defined to be $\rho(x', y', z')$, where

$$\rho = \lim_{\Delta V' \to 0} \frac{\Delta e}{\Delta V'}, \tag{5.10}$$

assuming that this limit exists and is independent of the shape of the element $\Delta V'$.

Let $P(x, y, z)$ be a point outside V. The potential at P due to the charge in $\Delta V'$ is, by (5.7), approximately

$$\frac{1}{4\pi\varepsilon_0} \frac{\rho(x', y', z')\, \Delta V'}{\{(x-x')^2 + (y-y')^2 + (z-z')^2\}^{\frac{1}{2}}}, \tag{5.11}$$

since $\rho(x', y', z')\, \Delta V'$ is the approximate quantity of charge contained within $\Delta V'$ (Fig. 5.2). On writing $\Delta V' = \Delta x'\, \Delta y'\, \Delta z'$, summing over all

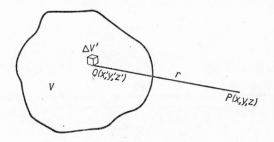

Fig. 5.2

volume elements, and proceeding to the limit as all $\Delta V' \to 0$, we get the expression for the potential ϕ at $P(x, y, z)$

$$\phi(x, y, z) = \frac{1}{4\pi\varepsilon_0} \iiint_{V'} \frac{\rho(x', y', z')\, dx'dy'dz'}{\{(x-x')^2 + (y-y')^2 + (z-z')^2\}^{\frac{1}{2}}}, \tag{5.12}$$

where the region of integration V' is simply V expressed in primed co-ordinates. More concisely we may write

$$\phi(P) = \frac{1}{4\pi\varepsilon_0} \int_{V'} \frac{\rho \, dV'}{r}, \tag{5.13}$$

where r is used to denote the distance from P to the differential element dV'.

When P is an interior point of V, the integral (5.12) is improper, since the denominator of the integrand vanishes when $(x', y', z') = (x, y, z)$. Nevertheless, it is possible to define the potential at an interior point P by imagining the charge in a small region containing P to be removed, forming a *cavity*. One defines $\phi(P)$ to be the (unique) limiting value obtained for the potential as the cavity is allowed to shrink to zero. Equation (5.12) again applies, provided that the integral is treated in like manner. A small spherical region centred at P is first removed from V' and the integral formed over the remainder. The limit of this integral as the radius of the excluded region tends to zero is equal to $\phi(P)$, and is called the *principal value* of the integral (5.12). The electric field $\mathbf{E}$ can also be defined at an interior point, by an appropriate limiting process, in such a way that the equation $\mathbf{E} = -\text{grad}\,\phi$ still applies. For further details, the reader should consult books on electromagnetic theory*.

The potential due to charge distributed continuously over a surface S or a line l can also be expressed in integral form. If the surface density (charge per unit area) at the point (x', y', z') on S is σ, then at a point P not on S, the potential is

$$\phi(P) = \frac{1}{4\pi\varepsilon_0} \int_{S'} \frac{\sigma \, dS'}{r}. \tag{5.14}$$

If the line density (charge per unit length) at the point (x', y', z') on l is λ, then at a point P not on l, the potential is

$$\phi(P) = \frac{1}{4\pi\varepsilon_0} \int_{l'} \frac{\lambda \, dl'}{r}. \tag{5.15}$$

(In each of (5.14) and (5.15), r denotes the distance from P to the differential element of charge, and primes denote that the region of integration is to be expressed in primed coordinates.)

In (5.14), a principal value of the integral may be used to define the potential at a point on the surface S. But line charges cannot be treated in this way because the potential of a line charge is always infinite at points on the line.

* See, for example, V. C. A. Ferraro, *Electromagnetic Theory* (Athlone Press, 1956), chapter V.

5.3 Gauss's Law

As a step towards the construction of differential equations for ϕ and $\mathbf{E}$, we derive a law relating the flux of $\mathbf{E}$, out through a general closed surface S in empty space, to the total electric charge Q contained in the volume bounded by S. This law, known as Gauss's law, states that

$$\int_S \mathbf{E}\,.\,d\mathbf{S} = \frac{Q}{\varepsilon_0}, \tag{5.16}$$

where the direction of $d\mathbf{S}$ is that of the outward drawn normal.

Proof. Consider first the case where the only charge enclosed by S is a point charge e at a point A. At any point of S with position vector $\mathbf{r}$ relative to A, we have by Coulomb's law

$$\mathbf{E} = \frac{e\hat{\mathbf{r}}}{4\pi\varepsilon_0 r^2}, \tag{5.17}$$

and

$$\int_S \mathbf{E}\,.\,d\mathbf{S} = \frac{e}{4\pi\varepsilon_0} \int_S \frac{\hat{\mathbf{r}}\,.\,d\mathbf{S}}{r^2}. \tag{5.18}$$

The integral on the right is the solid angle subtended at A by the surface S, and is equal to 4π, since A is an interior point. Therefore,

$$\int_S \mathbf{E}\,.\,d\mathbf{S} = \frac{e}{\varepsilon_0}. \tag{5.19}$$

This is Gauss's law for a single enclosed point charge.

If there are several point charges $e_1, e_2, \ldots, e_n$ enclosed by S, where

$$Q = \sum_{i=1}^{n} e_i,$$

then Gauss's law (5.16) is obtained by summing the contributions from the individual charges to the flux of $\mathbf{E}$. The result remains valid, also, if the enclosed charge is in the form of a continuous distribution.

Any charge *outside* S is to be neglected entirely in the calculation of Q in (5.16). For, if e now denotes a point charge at an exterior point, (5.18) is still valid. But since the solid angle subtended by a closed surface at an exterior point is zero, in this case the right hand side vanishes, and so the contribution to the outward flux of $\mathbf{E}$ through S from each exterior charge is zero.

Example. Charge of total amount e is distributed uniformly throughout the sphere $x^2+y^2+z^2 \leqslant a^2$, the rest of space being empty. Find the electrostatic field at any point.

Let $\mathbf{r} = x\mathbf{i}+y\mathbf{j}+z\mathbf{k}$. By symmetry, on any spherical surface $r = $ constant the field vector $\mathbf{E}$ has the same magnitude at all points, and is in the normal direction. Thus, we can write

$$\mathbf{E} = E(r)\hat{\mathbf{r}}, \tag{5.20}$$

where $E(r)$ is some function of r to be determined. Apply Gauss's law to the spherical surface S of radius r, where we first assume $r > a$. Then

$$\int_S \mathbf{E}.d\mathbf{S} = \frac{e}{\varepsilon_0}, \tag{5.21}$$

that is, by (5.20),

$$\int_S E(r)\hat{\mathbf{r}}.d\mathbf{S} = \int_S E(r)\hat{\mathbf{r}}.\hat{\mathbf{r}}\,dS = \int_S E(r)\,dS = \frac{e}{\varepsilon_0}, \tag{5.22}$$

since $d\mathbf{S} = \hat{\mathbf{r}}\,dS$ (Fig. 5.3) and $\hat{\mathbf{r}}.\hat{\mathbf{r}} = 1$.

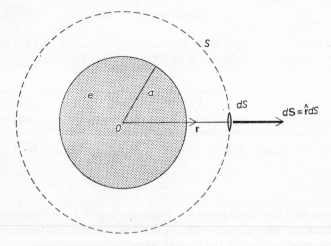

Fig. 5.3

Now, on S, $E(r)$ is a constant scalar and may therefore be taken outside of the third integral in (5.22). We get

$$\int_S E(r)\,dS = E(r)\int_S dS = E(r)4\pi r^2 = \frac{e}{\varepsilon_0}. \tag{5.23}$$

which determines $E(r)$. Therefore,

$$\mathbf{E} = E(r)\hat{\mathbf{r}} = \frac{e}{4\pi\varepsilon_0 r^2}\hat{\mathbf{r}}. \qquad (5.24)$$

This shows, incidentally, that the field at any point outside the distribution of charge is the same as if all the charge e were concentrated at the origin.

Now let $r \leqslant a$. A slight complication arises since this time the surface S passes through charge. However, the volume density of the given charge distribution is finite throughout the sphere, and so the amount of charge actually lying *in* the surface S is vanishingly small and need not be considered further. (This would not be the case, for example, if S passed through a *point charge*.)

As before,

$$\int_S \mathbf{E}.d\mathbf{S} = 4\pi r^2 E(r). \qquad (5.25)$$

The charge enclosed by S is proportional to the enclosed volume, and hence to r^3, since the density in the sphere $r \leqslant a$ is stated to be constant. Therefore, the charge within S is $r^3 e/a^3$, and so by Gauss's law and (5.25),

$$4\pi r^2 E(r) = \frac{r^3 e}{a^3 \varepsilon_0}.$$

The field $\mathbf{E}$ in the region $r \leqslant a$ is thus

$$\mathbf{E} = E(r)\hat{\mathbf{r}} = \frac{er}{4\pi a^3 \varepsilon_0}\hat{\mathbf{r}}. \qquad (5.26)$$

The potential may also be determined, if required, by using the formula

$$\mathbf{E} = -\operatorname{grad}\phi. \qquad (5.27)$$

Since $\operatorname{grad} 1/r = -(1/r^2)\hat{\mathbf{r}}$, we see by (5.24) that for $r > a$, the potential is

$$\phi = \frac{e}{4\pi\varepsilon_0 r}, \qquad (5.28)$$

where we have employed the convention $\phi = 0$ at $r = \infty$ to make ϕ unique.

In order to deal with the region $r \leqslant a$, we note that $\operatorname{grad} r^2 = 2r\hat{\mathbf{r}}$ (see 4.17), and so in order to satisfy (5.26) we must have

$$\phi = -\frac{er^2}{8\pi a^3 \varepsilon_0} + C, \qquad (5.29)$$

where C is a constant. This constant is determined by the condition that the potential is continuous at $r = a$ (otherwise its gradient would be infinite there, whereas we have found the field to be finite). Thus, expressions (5.28) and (5.29) must agree when r is put equal to a. This gives

$$C = \frac{3e}{8\pi\varepsilon_0 a},$$

and so the potential in $r \leqslant a$ is

$$\phi = \frac{e}{8\pi\varepsilon_0 a^3}(3a^2 - r^2).$$

Analogues of Gauss's law are found in many other physical contexts. In fluid mechanics, it is often convenient to identify the motion of a fluid in a region with that due to a certain hypothetical distribution of *sources* and *sinks*. A point source is a point at which new fluid enters the system at a constant rate and flows symmetrically in all directions. Its *strength* is $1/4\pi$ times the volume of fluid entering the system in unit time. A point sink is a point at which fluid likewise leaves the system. For incompressible fluids, the law corresponding to Gauss's law states, in mathematical terms, the evident fact that the volume rate of flow out through a closed surface S is equal to 4π times the total strength of the sources enclosed by S, where sinks are counted as sources of negative sign. If the fluid velocity vector is denoted by $\mathbf{q}$ and the total source strength by m, then it follows from the discussion in §3.8 that the stated law is

$$\int_S \mathbf{q} \cdot d\mathbf{S} = 4\pi m.$$

In the theory of heat conduction, the conservation of energy implies that the rate of flow of heat out through any closed surface, when temperatures in the interior are in a steady state, is equal to the total rate of production by any enclosed heat sources and sinks (nuclear, chemical, electrical, etc.) The *heat flow vector* $\mathbf{F}$ is in the direction of the flow at any point, and has magnitude equal to the quantity of heat per unit area, per unit time, crossing an element of surface normal to $\mathbf{F}$ at the point. If the total rate of heat production inside a closed surface S is M, then

$$\int_S \mathbf{F} \cdot d\mathbf{S} = M.$$

EXERCISES

1. A circle has its centre on the z axis and its plane perpendicular to Oz. Show that the solid angle that it subtends at O is $2\pi(1 - \cos\theta)$, where $\theta = P\hat{O}z$

and P is any point on the circle. Hence show that the flux, through the circle, of the electric field of a point charge e placed at O is

$$\frac{e}{2\varepsilon_0}(1-\cos\theta)$$

2.   Derive Coulomb's law, assuming the validity of Gauss's law.

3.   An electric point charge Q situated at the origin O is surrounded by an infinitely extended cloud of charge whose density at any point at distance r from O is $-\mu Qe^{-\mu r}/4\pi r^2$, where μ is a constant. Show, by applying Gauss's law over a sphere of arbitrary radius centred at O, that the magnitude of the electric field at any point is $Qe^{-\mu r}/4\pi\varepsilon_0 r^2$. (This model can be used as an approximation in describing certain properties of the atom.)

4.   If R denotes the usual cylindrical polar coordinate, show that $\operatorname{grad} R = \hat{\mathbf{R}}$, where $\hat{\mathbf{R}}$ is the unit vector in the direction R increasing. (Hint: Use the relation between the gradient of a scalar function and the greatest spatial rate of increase of the function.)

Consider an infinite straight line charge, whose line density is e, lying along the z axis. Apply Gauss's law to the surface of a closed circular cylinder of unit length and arbitrary radius, with z axis as cylinder axis, to prove that the (vacuum) electric field at any point of space is

$$\mathbf{E} = \frac{e}{2\pi\varepsilon_0 R}\hat{\mathbf{R}}.$$

Hence show that the electrostatic potential of the line charge may be taken as

$$\phi = -\frac{e}{2\pi\varepsilon_0}\ln R + const.$$

(Why is the condition $\phi = 0$ at infinity inapplicable in this case?)

5.   A limiting system of two electric point charges, $-e$ at A and e at B, where $e \to \infty$ and $AB \to 0$ in such a way that eAB tends to a finite limit m, is called an *electric dipole*. The limit vector

$$\mathbf{m} = \lim_{e\to\infty} e\overrightarrow{AB}$$

is called the *dipole moment*, and the limiting line AB is the *dipole axis*. If a dipole $\mathbf{m}$ is placed at the origin and has the z axis as dipole axis, show that the flux of its electric field through the circle in exercise 1 is $(m\sin^3\theta)/2a\varepsilon_0$, where a is the radius of the circle.

CHAPTER 6

Divergence; Gauss's Theorem

6.1 The Divergence of a Vector Point Function

So far, we have considered only the case where the operator ∇ acts on a scalar point function. It may also act on a vector point function $\mathbf{F}(x, y, z)$, and can do this in two ways. Firstly, it can act on $\mathbf{F}$ as a *scalar* product, giving the scalar function

$$\nabla . \mathbf{F} = \left(\mathbf{i}\frac{\partial}{\partial x} + \mathbf{j}\frac{\partial}{\partial y} + \mathbf{k}\frac{\partial}{\partial z} \right) . (F_x \mathbf{i} + F_y \mathbf{j} + F_z \mathbf{k})$$

$$= \frac{\partial F_x}{\partial x} + \frac{\partial F_y}{\partial y} + \frac{\partial F_z}{\partial z}, \tag{6.1}$$

where (F_x, F_y, F_z) are the components of $\mathbf{F}$, and we assume that $\mathbf{F}$ is differentiable in order that the partial derivatives of the components exist. Secondly, with the same conditions on $\mathbf{F}$, ∇ can act on $\mathbf{F}$ as a *vector* product, the result being the vector function

$$\nabla \wedge \mathbf{F} = \left(\mathbf{i}\frac{\partial}{\partial x} + \mathbf{j}\frac{\partial}{\partial y} + \mathbf{k}\frac{\partial}{\partial z} \right) \wedge (F_x \mathbf{i} + F_y \mathbf{j} + F_z \mathbf{k})$$

$$= \mathbf{i}\left(\frac{\partial F_z}{\partial y} - \frac{\partial F_y}{\partial z} \right) + \mathbf{j}\left(\frac{\partial F_x}{\partial z} - \frac{\partial F_z}{\partial x} \right) + \mathbf{k}\left(\frac{\partial F_y}{\partial x} - \frac{\partial F_x}{\partial y} \right). \tag{6.2}$$

The first of these expressions is called the *divergence* of $\mathbf{F}$, and is written $\operatorname{div} \mathbf{F}$,

$$\operatorname{div} \mathbf{F} = \nabla . \mathbf{F}. \tag{6.3}$$

The second expression is called the *curl* of $\mathbf{F}$,

$$\operatorname{curl} \mathbf{F} = \nabla \wedge \mathbf{F}. \tag{6.4}$$

Clearly, from the definitions, both divergence and curl are linear operators, i.e. if c_1 and c_2 are constants and $\mathbf{F}, \mathbf{G}$ are differentiable vector functions, then

$$\nabla.(c_1\,\mathbf{F}+c_2\,\mathbf{G}) = c_1\,\nabla.\mathbf{F}+c_2\,\nabla.\mathbf{G}$$

with a similar relation applying with (.) replaced by ($\wedge$). We shall be concerned here with the divergence of vector point functions, the curl operation being treated in the next chapter.

Note that $\nabla.\mathbf{F} \neq \mathbf{F}.\nabla$; the expression

$$\mathbf{F}.\nabla = F_x\frac{\partial}{\partial x}+F_y\frac{\partial}{\partial y}+F_z\frac{\partial}{\partial z}.$$

is an operator, while $\nabla.\mathbf{F}$ is a scalar function. When scalar products are formed with ∇, care must be taken to keep the correct order of factors.

Example. Find $\operatorname{div}(y^2z\mathbf{i}+xz\mathbf{j}-y^2\mathbf{k})$.

We have

$$\operatorname{div}(y^2z\mathbf{i}+xz\mathbf{j}-y^2\mathbf{k}) = \frac{\partial}{\partial x}(y^2z)+\frac{\partial}{\partial y}(xz)+\frac{\partial}{\partial z}(-y^2)$$

$$= 0+0+0 = 0.$$

This example shows that the equation $\operatorname{div}\mathbf{F} = 0$ does not have only trivial solutions such as $\mathbf{F} = 0$ or $\mathbf{F} = $ a constant vector.

Definition. A vector point function $\mathbf{F}$ such that $\operatorname{div}\mathbf{F} = 0$ is called *solenoidal* or *divergence-free*.

The following identity is useful in dealing with divergences. Let $\phi(x,y,z)$ and $\mathbf{F}(x,y,z)$ be differentiable functions. Then

$$\operatorname{div}(\phi\mathbf{F}) = \phi\operatorname{div}\mathbf{F}+(\operatorname{grad}\phi).\mathbf{F}. \tag{6.5}$$

For, if $\mathbf{F} = F_x\mathbf{i}+F_y\mathbf{j}+F_z\mathbf{k}$, then

$$\operatorname{div}(\phi\mathbf{F}) = \frac{\partial}{\partial x}(\phi F_x)+\frac{\partial}{\partial y}(\phi F_y)+\frac{\partial}{\partial z}(\phi F_z)$$

$$= \phi\frac{\partial F_x}{\partial x}+\frac{\partial\phi}{\partial x}F_x+\phi\frac{\partial F_y}{\partial y}+\frac{\partial\phi}{\partial y}F_y+\phi\frac{\partial F_z}{\partial z}+\frac{\partial\phi}{\partial z}F_z$$

$$= \phi\left(\frac{\partial F_x}{\partial x}+\frac{\partial F_y}{\partial y}+\frac{\partial F_z}{\partial z}\right)+\frac{\partial\phi}{\partial x}F_x+\frac{\partial\phi}{\partial y}F_y+\frac{\partial\phi}{\partial z}F_z$$

$$= \phi\operatorname{div}\mathbf{F}+\operatorname{grad}\phi.\mathbf{F}.$$

In ∇ notation, we have

$$\nabla.(\phi\mathbf{F}) = \phi\nabla.\mathbf{F}+(\nabla\phi).\mathbf{F} \tag{6.6}$$

G

Note the similarity here with the formula for differentiating a product of two functions of one variable in elementary calculus. To remember (6.6), use the facts that

(i) ∇ is a *differential* operator, and so there appear two terms on the right, in which ∇ acts in turn on one of the functions ϕ and $\mathbf{F}$ while the other is not differentiated.

(ii) ∇ is a *vector* operator, and its product with a vector function must be in the form of a scalar product or a vector product. It is easy to see from the derivation of (6.6), how the scalar product on the left leads to the appearance of a scalar product in each term on the right.

Many of the ∇ identities to be met later can be remembered by similar arguments.

Example. If $\mathbf{r} = x\mathbf{i} + y\mathbf{j} + z\mathbf{k}$, show that div $\mathbf{r} = 3$, and calculate $\text{div}(r^n\hat{\mathbf{r}})$ where n is any real number.

We have

$$\text{div}\,\mathbf{r} = \nabla.\mathbf{r}$$

$$= \frac{\partial}{\partial x}x + \frac{\partial}{\partial y}y + \frac{\partial}{\partial z}z$$

$$= 1+1+1 = 3. \tag{6.7}$$

To calculate $\text{div}(r^n\hat{\mathbf{r}})$, we use the identity (6.6). It is simplest to avoid differentiation of the unit vector $\hat{\mathbf{r}}$, and instead write

$$\nabla.(r^n\hat{\mathbf{r}}) = \nabla.(r^{n-1}\mathbf{r}) = r^{n-1}\nabla.\mathbf{r} + (\nabla r^{n-1}).\mathbf{r}.$$

But, we have found that $\nabla.\mathbf{r} = 3$. Also, by the rule (4.17),

$$\nabla r^{n-1} = (n-1)r^{n-2}\hat{\mathbf{r}}.$$

Therefore,

$$\nabla.(r^n\hat{\mathbf{r}}) = 3r^{n-1} + (n-1)r^{n-2}\hat{\mathbf{r}}.\mathbf{r}$$

$$= 3r^{n-1} + (n-1)r^{n-1}$$

$$= (n+2)r^{n-1}. \tag{6.8}$$

6.2 The Operator ∇^2

The gradient of a twice differentiable scalar point function ϕ is a vector (point function), and the divergence of such vectors is frequently encountered in practice. We have

$$\text{grad}\,\phi = \frac{\partial\phi}{\partial x}\mathbf{i} + \frac{\partial\phi}{\partial y}\mathbf{j} + \frac{\partial\phi}{\partial z}\mathbf{k},$$

and

$$\text{div grad}\, \phi = \frac{\partial}{\partial x}\left(\frac{\partial \phi}{\partial x}\right) + \frac{\partial}{\partial y}\left(\frac{\partial \phi}{\partial y}\right) + \frac{\partial}{\partial z}\left(\frac{\partial \phi}{\partial z}\right)$$

$$= \frac{\partial^2 \phi}{\partial x^2} + \frac{\partial^2 \phi}{\partial y^2} + \frac{\partial^2 \phi}{\partial z^2}. \tag{6.9}$$

In ∇ notation, this is written $\nabla^2 \phi$, where ∇^2 is the operator

$$\nabla^2 = \nabla.\nabla = \frac{\partial}{\partial x}\frac{\partial}{\partial x} + \frac{\partial}{\partial y}\frac{\partial}{\partial y} + \frac{\partial}{\partial z}\frac{\partial}{\partial z}$$

$$= \frac{\partial^2}{\partial x^2} + \frac{\partial^2}{\partial y^2} + \frac{\partial^2}{\partial z^2}. \tag{6.10}$$

It should be observed that

$$\nabla^2 \equiv \text{div grad}$$

only when the operator ∇^2 acts on a scalar. When ∇^2 acts on a vector $\mathbf{F} = F_x \mathbf{i} + F_y \mathbf{j} + F_z \mathbf{k}$ we have

$$\nabla^2 \mathbf{F} = \left(\frac{\partial^2}{\partial x^2} + \frac{\partial^2}{\partial y^2} + \frac{\partial^2}{\partial z^2}\right)(F_x \mathbf{i} + F_y \mathbf{j} + F_z \mathbf{k})$$

$$= \mathbf{i}\, \nabla^2 F_x + \mathbf{j}\, \nabla^2 F_y + \mathbf{k}\, \nabla^2 F_z, \tag{6.11}$$

which is meaningful but not equal to $\text{div}\,(\text{grad}\,\mathbf{F})$, because $\text{grad}\,\mathbf{F}$ has not been defined.

Example. Calculate $\nabla^2 f(r)$ where f is a twice differentiable function of $r = (x^2 + y^2 + z^2)^{\frac{1}{2}}$. Find all $f(r)$ such that $\nabla^2 f = 0$.

By (4.17), we have

$$\nabla^2 f(r) = \nabla.\{\nabla f(r)\} = \nabla.\left(\frac{df}{dr}\hat{\mathbf{r}}\right)$$

$$= \nabla.\left(\frac{1}{r}\frac{df}{dr}\mathbf{r}\right) = \frac{1}{r}\frac{df}{dr}\nabla.\mathbf{r} + \nabla\left(\frac{1}{r}\frac{df}{dr}\right).\mathbf{r}.$$

But $\nabla.\mathbf{r} = 3$, and

$$\nabla\left(\frac{1}{r}\frac{df}{dr}\right) = \left\{\frac{d}{dr}\left(\frac{1}{r}\frac{df}{dr}\right)\right\}\hat{\mathbf{r}} = \left(\frac{1}{r}\frac{d^2f}{dr^2} - \frac{1}{r^2}\frac{df}{dr}\right)\hat{\mathbf{r}}.$$

Therefore,

$$\nabla^2 f(r) = \frac{3}{r}\frac{df}{dr} + \left(\frac{1}{r}\frac{d^2f}{dr^2} - \frac{1}{r^2}\frac{df}{dr}\right)\hat{\mathbf{r}}.\mathbf{r}$$

$$= \frac{d^2f}{dr^2} + \frac{2}{r}\frac{df}{dr}. \tag{6.12}$$

For the second part of the question, put $u = df/dr$. By the last result, we have to solve

$$\frac{du}{dr} + \frac{2}{r}u = 0,$$

i.e., on multiplying by r^2,

$$\frac{d}{dr}(r^2 u) = 0,$$

whence

$$r^2 u = C, \qquad u = \frac{df}{dr} = \frac{C}{r^2},$$

and so on integrating we get

$$f = \frac{A}{r} + B, \tag{6.13}$$

where $A \, (= -C)$ and B are arbitrary constants. This is the most general solution for $f = f(r)$ of the equation $\nabla^2 f = 0$.

6.3   Gauss's Divergence Theorem

Frequently, the divergence of a vector occurs in a physical equation as a consequence of an integral *law* (such as Gauss's law in electrostatics) and an integral *theorem*. This theorem, known as Gauss's theorem, is the subject of the present section.

We shall refer to a closed surface as *simple* if it does not meet itself and if it can be deformed continuously (i.e. without 'tearing') into a sphere. Thus, an ellipsoid is a simple closed surface, but the surface of an anchor ring (torus) is not. (Fig. 8.7.)

Gauss's Theorem. Let S be a simple closed surface enclosing a region V, and suppose that no line parallel to any one of the coordinate axes meets S in more than two points. Let $\mathbf{F} = F_x \mathbf{i} + F_y \mathbf{j} + F_z \mathbf{k}$ be a vector point function which is continuous and has continuous first partial derivatives everywhere in V and on S. Then

$$\int_S \mathbf{F} \cdot d\mathbf{S} = \int_V \operatorname{div} \mathbf{F} \, dV, \tag{6.14}$$

where the outward normal direction is taken for $d\mathbf{S}$.

Proof. Denote by S_0 the projection of S on the xy plane. Two points of S project onto each interior point (x, y) of S_0; call their z coordinates $z_1(x, y)$ and $z_2(x, y)$, where $z_2 > z_1$ (Fig. 6.1). Consider

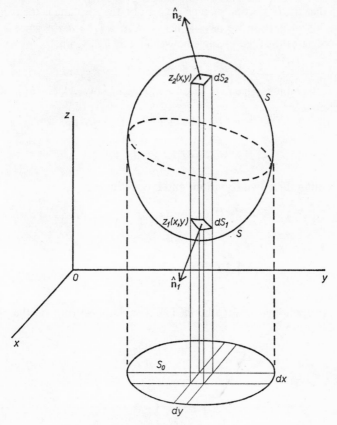

Fig. 6.1

$$\int_V \frac{\partial F_z}{\partial z}\, dV = \iiint_V \frac{\partial F_z}{\partial z}\, dx\, dy\, dz$$

$$= \iint_{S_0} \left(\int_{z_1}^{z_2} \frac{\partial F_z}{\partial z}\, dz \right) dx\, dy$$

$$= \iint_{S_0} \left| F_z \right|_{z_1}^{z_2} dx\, dy$$

$$= \iint_{S_0} \{ F_z(x, y, z_2(x, y)) - F_z(x, y, z_1(x, y)) \}\, dx\, dy. \qquad (6.15)$$

We shall prove that this integral is equal to $\int_S F_z \mathbf{k} \cdot d\mathbf{S}$. Let dS_1 and dS_2 be elements of S, containing the points (x, y, z_1), (x, y, z_2) respectively, such that the projection of each element on the xy plane is the rectangle $dxdy$. By projection we have $\mathbf{k} . d\mathbf{S}_2 = \mathbf{k} . \hat{\mathbf{n}}_2 \, dS_2 = dxdy$, since $\mathbf{k} . \hat{\mathbf{n}}_2$ is the cosine of the (acute) angle between $\mathbf{k}$ and $\hat{\mathbf{n}}_2$. Again,

$$\mathbf{k} . d\mathbf{S}_1 = \mathbf{k} . \hat{\mathbf{n}}_1 \, dS_1 = -dxdy,$$

where the minus sign enters because the angle between $\mathbf{k}$ and $\hat{\mathbf{n}}_1$ is obtuse. Therefore,

$$F_z \mathbf{k} . d\mathbf{S}_1 = -F_z(x, y, z_1(x, y)) \, dxdy,$$

and

$$F_z \mathbf{k} . d\mathbf{S}_2 = F_z(x, y, z_2(x, y)) \, dxdy.$$

On adding these two equations and integrating we get

$$\int_S F_z \mathbf{k} . d\mathbf{S} = \iint_{S_0} \{F_z(x, y, z_2(x, y)) - F_z(x, y, z_1(x, y))\} \, dxdy$$

$$= \int_V \frac{\partial F_z}{\partial z} \, dV, \tag{6.16}$$

by (6.15).

Corresponding results obtained by projection in turn on the yz and zx planes are

$$\int_S F_x \mathbf{i} . d\mathbf{S} = \int_V \frac{\partial F_x}{\partial x} \, dV, \tag{6.17}$$

$$\int_S F_y \mathbf{j} . d\mathbf{S} = \int_V \frac{\partial F_y}{\partial y} \, dV. \tag{6.18}$$

On adding (6.16), (6.17) and (6.18) and using the definition

$$\operatorname{div} \mathbf{F} = \frac{\partial F_x}{\partial x} + \frac{\partial F_y}{\partial y} + \frac{\partial F_z}{\partial z},$$

we get, as required,

$$\int_S \mathbf{F} . d\mathbf{S} = \int_V \operatorname{div} \mathbf{F} \, dV.$$

For many applications it is necessary to extend the theorem to include regions bounded by more general, non-simple surfaces. The last equation again holds in such cases provided that the normal direction for each element $d\mathbf{S}$ is always that which points away from the enclosed volume. Figure 6.2 shows a typical case, S' being a simple surface enclosed within a non-simple surface S''. The region V, as shown, is bounded by the two surfaces S' and S'' which are jointly denoted by S.

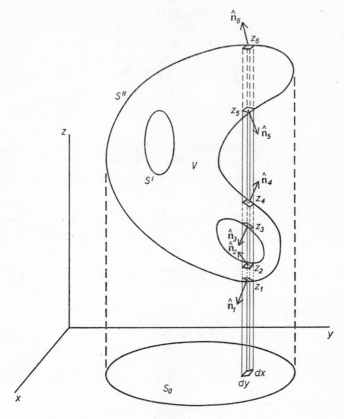

Fig. 6.2

In the notation of the diagram, the argument leading to (6.15) now gives

$$\int_V \frac{\partial F_z}{\partial z}\, dV = \iiint_V \frac{\partial F_z}{\partial z}\, dx\,dy\,dz$$

$$= \iint_{S_0} \left\{ \left| F_z \right|_{z_1}^{z_2} + \left| F_z \right|_{z_3}^{z_4} + \dots \right\} dx\,dy. \qquad (6.19)$$

On taking account of whether a normal vector makes an acute or an obtuse angle with $\mathbf{k}$, we get

$$\begin{aligned}
\left\{ \left| F_z \right|_{z_1}^{z_2} + \left| F_z \right|_{z_3}^{z_4} + \dots \right\} dx\,dy = {} & -F_z(x, y, z_1)\mathbf{k} \cdot \hat{\mathbf{n}}_1\, dS_1 + F_z(x, y, z_2)\mathbf{k} \cdot \hat{\mathbf{n}}_2\, dS_2 \\
& -F_z(x, y, z_3)\mathbf{k} \cdot \hat{\mathbf{n}}_3\, dS_3 \\
& +F_z(x, y, z_4)\mathbf{k} \cdot \hat{\mathbf{n}}_4\, dS_4 - \dots. \qquad (6.20)
\end{aligned}$$

As the base point (x, y) varies, covering S_0, the points $(x, y, z_1), (x, y, z_2), \ldots$ cover the whole of the surface S, and so by (6.19) and (6.20) we obtain on integration

$$\int_V \frac{\partial F_z}{\partial z} \, dV = \int_S F_z \mathbf{k} . d\mathbf{S},$$

as in (6.16). The proof now proceeds as before.

The need to consider non-simple surfaces when applying Gauss's theorem arises in some quite elementary physical problems. For example, suppose we attempt to apply the theorem to the electrostatic field vector $\mathbf{E}$ of a point charge e situated at the origin O, where S is to be a sphere centred at O. Then, as in (5.4),

$$\mathbf{E} = \frac{e}{4\pi\varepsilon_0 r^2} \hat{\mathbf{r}},$$

and

$$\operatorname{div} \mathbf{E} = \frac{e}{4\pi\varepsilon_0} \operatorname{div}(r^{-2}\hat{\mathbf{r}}) = 0, \qquad (6.21)$$

by (6.8). But, by Gauss's *law*,

$$\int_S \mathbf{E} . d\mathbf{S} = \frac{e}{\varepsilon_0}. \qquad (6.22)$$

It thus appears from (6.21) and (6.22) that Gauss's theorem is violated, because the volume integral of $\operatorname{div} \mathbf{E}$, according to (6.21), is zero.

The reason for the apparent breakdown is that the vector $\mathbf{E}$ does not satisfy the conditions in the statement of Gauss's theorem at all points enclosed by S, because $\mathbf{E}$ is not continuous at O. Indeed, (6.21) is valid only for $r \neq 0$. To apply Gauss's theorem correctly, we must exclude the origin from the volume region V, and this can be done by surrounding O by a small sphere S_1. Let V' denote the region between S_1 and S. Therefore,

$$\int_{V'} \operatorname{div} \mathbf{E} \, dV = \int_S \mathbf{E} . d\mathbf{S} + \int_{S_1} \mathbf{E} . d\mathbf{S}_1 = 0, \qquad (6.23)$$

since $\operatorname{div} \mathbf{E} = 0$ in V'. We now have agreement with (6.22), because Gauss's law applied separately to S_1 gives

$$\int_{S_1} \mathbf{E} . d\mathbf{S}_1 = -e/\varepsilon_0$$

where the minus sign arises when $d\mathbf{S}_1$ points towards the origin (away from V'). In the same way, any finite number of points at which a field vector violates the conditions of Gauss's theorem can be (and must be) excluded from the region of integration before the theorem is applied.

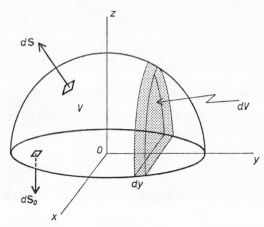

Fig. 6.3

Example. Use Gauss's theorem to evaluate

$$\int_S \mathbf{F}.d\mathbf{S},$$

where $\mathbf{F} = 2xy^2\mathbf{i}+z^3\mathbf{j}-x^2y\mathbf{k}$ and S is the curved surface of the hemisphere $x^2+y^2+z^2 = a^2$, $z > 0$.

The surface S given in the question is *open*. To form a closed surface in order to apply the theorem, we may combine S and S_0, where S_0 is the base of the hemisphere, $x^2+y^2 \leqslant a^2$, $z = 0$. Denote the enclosed hemispherical region by V (Fig. 6.3). Then

$$\int_S \mathbf{F}.d\mathbf{S}+\int_{S_0} \mathbf{F}.d\mathbf{S}_0 = \int_V \operatorname{div}\mathbf{F}\,dV$$

and so

$$\int_S \mathbf{F}.d\mathbf{S} = \int_V \operatorname{div}\mathbf{F}\,dV-\int_{S_0} \mathbf{F}.d\mathbf{S}_0. \tag{6.24}$$

We need to evaluate the two integrals on the right, where

$$\operatorname{div}\mathbf{F} = \frac{\partial}{\partial x}(2xy^2)+\frac{\partial}{\partial y}(z^3)+\frac{\partial}{\partial z}(-x^2y) = 2y^2.$$

Let V be subdivided into semi-circular elements by a family of planes perpendicular to the y axis. The radius of such an element, situated at y, is $(a^2-y^2)^{\frac{1}{2}}$, and so we can replace dV by $\frac{1}{2}\pi(a^2-y^2)\,dy$, obtaining

$$\int_V \text{div } \mathbf{F} \, dV = \int_{-a}^a 2y^2 . \tfrac{1}{2}\pi(a^2 - y^2) dy$$

$$= 2\pi \int_0^a y^2(a^2 - y^2) \, dy$$

$$= 2\pi \left| \frac{a^2 y^3}{3} - \frac{y^5}{5} \right|_0^a = \frac{4\pi a^5}{15}.$$

The integral over S_0 is easily evaluated, because $d\mathbf{S}_0 = -\mathbf{k} \, dS_0$, and therefore

$$\int_{S_0} \mathbf{F} . d\mathbf{S}_0 = \int_{S_0} \mathbf{F} . (-\mathbf{k}) \, dS_0 = \int_{S_0} x^2 y \, dS_0$$

$$= \int_{-a}^a \int_{-\sqrt{(a^2 - x^2)}}^{\sqrt{(a^2 - x^2)}} x^2 y \, dx dy = 0,$$

as we easily find on performing the y integration first. Hence, by (6.24),

$$\int_S \mathbf{F} . d\mathbf{S} = \frac{4\pi a^5}{15}.$$

This method of calculating the flux of a vector field $\mathbf{F}$ across an open surface is useful if the flux across a second open surface with the same boundary is simpler to calculate, and if it is easy to integrate $\text{div } \mathbf{F}$ over the volume enclosed by the two open surfaces.

Example. Prove the identity

$$\int_S p \, d\mathbf{S} = \int_V \text{grad} \, p \, dV,$$

where p is a continuously differentiable scalar point function and S, $d\mathbf{S}$ and V have the same meanings as in Gauss's theorem.

Let $\hat{\mathbf{a}}$ be any constant unit vector. Observe that

$$\hat{\mathbf{a}} . \int_S p \, d\mathbf{S} = \hat{\mathbf{a}} . \int_S p\hat{\mathbf{n}} \, dS = \int_S \hat{\mathbf{a}} . p\hat{\mathbf{n}} \, dS,$$

because (by definition of a surface integral) the second expression is of the form

$$\hat{\mathbf{a}} . \left(\lim_{N \to \infty} \sum_{i=1}^N p_i \hat{\mathbf{n}}_i \, \Delta S_i \right) = \lim_{N \to \infty} \sum_{i=1}^N \hat{\mathbf{a}} . p_i \hat{\mathbf{n}}_i \, \Delta S_i,$$

which is equal to the third integral. Thus,

$$\hat{\mathbf{a}} . \int_S p \, d\mathbf{S} = \int_S p\hat{\mathbf{a}} . d\mathbf{S} = \int_V \nabla . (p\hat{\mathbf{a}}) \, dV$$

$$= \int_V \{p\nabla . \hat{\mathbf{a}} + (\nabla p) . \hat{\mathbf{a}}\} \, dV,$$

where we have used Gauss's theorem and the identity (6.5). Since $\hat{\mathbf{a}}$ is a constant vector, $\nabla . \hat{\mathbf{a}} = 0$. Also by a similar argument to that used above, $\hat{\mathbf{a}}$ may be taken outside of the last integral, and we get

$$\hat{\mathbf{a}} . \int_S p \, d\mathbf{S} = \hat{\mathbf{a}} . \int_V \operatorname{grad} p \, dV,$$

whence

$$\int_S p \, d\mathbf{S} = \int_V \operatorname{grad} p \, dV, \tag{6.25}$$

because the two sides have equal components in any direction $\hat{\mathbf{a}}$.

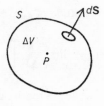

Fig. 6.4

6.4 Alternative Definition of Divergence

Let P be any point in a region in which there is a vector field $\mathbf{F}$, which satisfies the conditions of Gauss's theorem, so that $\operatorname{div} \mathbf{F}$ is continuous. Let S be any closed surface enclosing an elementary volume ΔV, of which P is a point (Fig. 6.4). Then, according to Gauss's theorem

$$\int_{\Delta V} \operatorname{div} \mathbf{F} \, dV = \int_S \mathbf{F} . d\mathbf{S}. \tag{6.26}$$

Now, since $\operatorname{div} \mathbf{F}$ is continuous, its value at any point $Q(x, y, z)$ in ΔV is near to its value at P. More precisely,

$$\operatorname{div} \mathbf{F} = (\operatorname{div} \mathbf{F})_P + \varepsilon(x, y, z),$$

where $\varepsilon \to 0$ as $Q \to P$. Therefore, on integrating over ΔV,

$$\int\limits_{\Delta V} \operatorname{div} \mathbf{F} \, dV = \int\limits_{\Delta V} (\operatorname{div} \mathbf{F})_P \, dV + \int\limits_{\Delta V} \varepsilon \, dV$$

$$= (\operatorname{div} \mathbf{F})_P \, \Delta V + \int\limits_{\Delta V} \varepsilon \, dV \qquad (6.27)$$

since $(\operatorname{div} \mathbf{F})_P$ is a constant in the integration and may be taken outside the integral sign.

On equating the two expressions (6.26), (6.27) for the integral of $\operatorname{div} \mathbf{F}$, and dividing by ΔV, we get

$$(\operatorname{div} \mathbf{F})_P = \frac{1}{\Delta V} \int\limits_{S} \mathbf{F} \cdot d\mathbf{S} - \frac{1}{\Delta V} \int\limits_{\Delta V} \varepsilon \, dV. \qquad (6.28)$$

We wish to show that the second term on the right in (6.28) tends to zero as all the dimensions of ΔV tend to zero. In fact, the magnitude of this term does not exceed

$$\frac{1}{\Delta V} \int\limits_{\Delta V} \bar{\varepsilon} \, dV = \bar{\varepsilon} \frac{1}{\Delta V} \int\limits_{\Delta V} dV = \bar{\varepsilon} \frac{1}{\Delta V} \Delta V = \bar{\varepsilon},$$

where $\bar{\varepsilon}$ is the maximum magnitude of ε in ΔV, and $\bar{\varepsilon} \to 0$ as $\Delta V \to 0$. Hence,

$$(\operatorname{div} \mathbf{F})_P = \lim_{\Delta V \to 0} \frac{1}{\Delta V} \int\limits_{S} \mathbf{F} \cdot d\mathbf{S}. \qquad (6.29)$$

This formula may be used as an alternative definition of the divergence of a vector $\mathbf{F}$ at a general point P, and states that the divergence is the 'outward flux per unit volume' at the point.

We have seen that in incompressible fluid dynamics the flux of the velocity vector out through a closed surface is equal to 4π times the total strength of the enclosed sources (see p. 90), and so its divergence is equal to 4π times the source strength per unit volume at any point. The term *divergence* is thus explained, because flow lines *diverge* from sources and not from other points, as is intuitively evident. The analogous relation between the divergence of the electrostatic field vector $\mathbf{E}$ and the volume density ρ of electric charge is obtained in the next section. Similar results apply for various other physical fields, such as in magnetism and Newtonian gravitation.

The formula (6.29) shows that the divergence of a vector, as defined in (6.1), is *invariant* with respect to transformations of rectangular cartesian coordinates, since the integral clearly depends in no way on a particular choice of axes. The significance of invariance was explained briefly in §4.2.

It is worth noting that although (6.29) may be taken as a definition of divergence, instead of (6.3), (in which case the proof of Gauss's theorem is found to be somewhat simpler), this involves the assumption, by no means trivial, that the limit in (6.29) is independent of the limiting shape of the element ΔV.

6.5 The Electrostatic Field Equations

By Gauss's law, if S is a closed surface *in vacuo* and e is the enclosed charge, then the electrostatic field vector $\mathbf{E}$ satisfies

$$\int_S \mathbf{E} . d\mathbf{S} = e/\varepsilon_0.$$

In the case where the charge e is in the form of a continuous distribution with volume density $\rho(x, y, z)$, we have

$$e = \int_V \rho \, dV,$$

and hence by applying the divergence theorem to the above surface integral (assuming that div $\mathbf{E}$ is continuous)

$$\int_V \operatorname{div} \mathbf{E} \, dV = \frac{1}{\varepsilon_0} \int_V \rho \, dV, \tag{6.30}$$

Since this is true for every volume region V, it follows that

$$\operatorname{div} \mathbf{E} = \rho/\varepsilon_0 \tag{6.31}$$

This last statement may be proved formally as follows. By (6.30)

$$\int_V \{\operatorname{div} \mathbf{E} - (\rho/\varepsilon_0)\} \, dV = 0 \tag{6.32}$$

for every volume V. We wish to show that this implies that the integrand vanishes identically. If this were *not* so, suppose that Q is a point at which div $\mathbf{E} - (\rho/\varepsilon_0) \neq 0$. Then, because this function is continuous, there is a neighbourhood N of Q in which div $\mathbf{E} - (\rho/\varepsilon_0)$ has the same sign as at Q. Suppose that the sign is positive. Then if V is put equal to N, the integrand in (6.32) is positive throughout the region of integration, and this contradicts the fact that the integral vanishes. A similar argument proves that div $\mathbf{E} - (\rho/\varepsilon_0)$ cannot be negative at Q, and so (6.31) must be valid at all points.

Equation (6.31) is a fundamental equation of the electrostatic field. It is to be regarded as a differential form of Gauss's law, which may be recovered by integration over an arbitrary volume.

If we introduce the electrostatic potential by the relation $\mathbf{E} = -\operatorname{grad}\phi$, then (6.31) takes the form

$$\nabla^2\phi = -\rho/\varepsilon_0, \tag{6.33}$$

which is known as *Poisson's equation*. This equation, when ρ is a given function of position, determines ϕ uniquely only when suitable data are specified on the boundary of the region under consideration, as we shall see in §7.2. If the region is the whole of space, and the boundary condition is chosen to be $\phi(x, y, z) \to 0$ as the point (x, y, z) tends to infinity, then the solution is as given in §5.2,

$$\phi(x, y, z) = \frac{1}{4\pi\varepsilon_0} \iiint\limits_{V'} \frac{\rho(x', y', z')\, dx'dy'dz'}{\{(x-x')^2 + (y-y')^2 + (z-z')^2\}^{\frac{1}{2}}}, \tag{6.34}$$

where V' is the region, expressed in primed coordinates, occupied by charge.

In any part of space in which $\rho = 0$, Poisson's equation reduces to

$$\nabla^2\phi = 0, \tag{6.35}$$

which is known as *Laplace's equation*. Laplace's equation is one of the most important equations in the whole of physics, and arises in many contexts. It is satisfied, in appropriate circumstances, by potential functions in fluid mechanics (see the next section), magnetism, heat theory, Newtonian gravitational theory, etc. Its study has been the basis of a great deal of research in the theory of partial differential equations.

6.6 The Equation of Continuity of a Fluid

When there are no sources or sinks in a region of fluid, the rate of flow of mass out through a closed surface S, inside the fluid and fixed in space, is equal to the rate of decrease of the mass of fluid enclosed within S. This is a kinematical consequence of the law of conservation of mass.

If $\mathbf{q}(x, y, z, t)$ denotes the fluid velocity and $\rho(x, y, z, t)$ the density at the point (x, y, z) at time t, then the rate of outward flow of mass is

$$\int_S \rho\mathbf{q}.d\mathbf{S},$$

as was shown in §3.8. Let V denote the volume region bounded by S.

Then, at time t, the mass contained in V is $\int_V \rho \, dV$, and so the rate of *increase* of mass in V is

$$\frac{d}{dt} \int_V \rho \, dV = \int_V \frac{\partial \rho}{\partial t} \, dV$$

by differentiation under the integral sign. (Alternatively, one may say that the mass in a fixed element of space ΔV, situated at (x, y, z), is $\rho(x, y, z, t) \Delta V$ at time t. The rate of increase of mass in the element is obtained by differentiation with respect to t, with x, y, z and ΔV kept constant, and is therefore $(\partial \rho / \partial t) \Delta V$. On summing over all elements ΔV, of V, and proceeding to the limit as all $\Delta V \to 0$, we again obtain $\int_V (\partial \rho / \partial t) \, dV$ as the rate of increase of mass in V.) Therefore, by conservation of mass we get

$$-\int_V \frac{\partial \rho}{\partial t} \, dV = \int_S \rho \mathbf{q} \cdot d\mathbf{S} = \int_V \nabla \cdot (\rho \mathbf{q}) \, dV,$$

by Gauss's theorem. Therefore,

$$\int_V \left\{ \frac{\partial \rho}{\partial t} + \nabla \cdot (\rho \mathbf{q}) \right\} dV = 0,$$

and since this is true for every space region V, we have (by the argument used in the last section)

$$\frac{\partial \rho}{\partial t} + \nabla \cdot (\rho \mathbf{q}) = 0. \tag{6.36}$$

This is called the *equation of continuity*, and holds at all points of a fluid where there are no sources or sinks.

If ρ is a constant in time and space (i.e. we consider an incompressible, homogeneous fluid), then (6.36) reduces to

$$\nabla \cdot \mathbf{q} = 0.$$

When $\mathbf{q}$ is a conservative field vector, there exists a *velocity potential* ϕ such that $\mathbf{q} = -\nabla \phi$, and the last equation becomes

$$\nabla^2 \phi = 0,$$

which we recognize as Laplace's equation.

EXERCISES

1.   If $\mathbf{F} = x^2y\mathbf{i} - 3y^2z^3\mathbf{j} + xyz\mathbf{k}$, find div $\mathbf{F}$ at the point $(-1, 2, 1)$.

2.   Given that $\phi = x^2y\cos z$, find $\nabla^2\phi$ at the point $(2, -1, 0)$.

3.   Show that div$(r^n\mathbf{r}) = (n+3)r^n$, where $\mathbf{r} = x\mathbf{i} + y\mathbf{j} + z\mathbf{k}$ and n is any constant.

4.   Prove, by means of Gauss's theorem, that $\frac{1}{3}\int \mathbf{r}.\hat{\mathbf{n}}\,dS$ evaluated over a closed surface S is equal to the volume enclosed within S. Hence verify your answers to exercise 7, Chapter 3.

5.   Prove that

$$\oint_C \operatorname{div}\mathbf{A}\operatorname{grad}\phi.\,d\mathbf{r} = -\oint_C \phi\operatorname{grad}(\operatorname{div}\mathbf{A}).\,d\mathbf{r},$$

where C is any closed curve in a given region R in which ϕ and $\mathbf{A}$ are single valued and continuous, ϕ possesses continuous first partial derivatives and $\mathbf{A}$ possesses continuous first and second partial derivatives.

6.   Use Gauss's theorem to calculate the flux of the vector field $\mathbf{F} = xy^2\mathbf{i} + y^3\mathbf{j} + y^2z\mathbf{k}$ out through the closed surface formed by the cylinder $x^2 + y^2 = 9$ and the planes $z = 0, z = 2$.

7.   If ϕ and $\mathbf{F}$ are continuous point functions with continuous first partial derivatives, prove that

$$\int_V \mathbf{F}.\operatorname{grad}\phi\,dV = \int_S \phi\mathbf{F}.\,d\mathbf{S} - \int_V \phi\operatorname{div}\mathbf{F}\,dV$$

where S is a closed surface enclosing the volume V.

8.   Evaluate $\int_S \operatorname{curl}\mathbf{F}.\,d\mathbf{S}$, where S is the open surface of the hemisphere $x^2 + y^2 + z^2 = a^2$, $z > 0$, and $\mathbf{F} = y\mathbf{i} + zx\mathbf{j} + y\mathbf{k}$, (i) by direct integration, (ii) by use of Gauss's theorem.

9.   A family of surfaces whose equations may be written $\phi(x, y, z) = const.$, where ϕ is any solution of Laplace's equation $\nabla^2\phi = 0$, are said to be *equipotential surfaces*. Show that a necessary and sufficient condition for a given family of surfaces $f(x, y, z) = const.$, where f is a single valued twice differentiable function, to be equipotential surfaces is that $\nabla^2 f/(\nabla f)^2$ is a function of f only. (Hint: $\phi = $ constant when $f = $ constant implies that there is a function G, of one variable, such that $\phi = G(f)$.)

Show that when the condition is satisfied, the potential function ϕ is given by

$$\phi = A\int \exp\left\{-\int \frac{\nabla^2 f}{(\nabla f)^2}\,df\right\}df + B,$$

where A and B are arbitrary constants.

10.   Use the results of exercise 9 to show that the families of surfaces (i) $x^2 + y^2 = const.$, (ii) $y/x = const.$ $(x \neq 0)$, (iii) $(x^2 + y^2)e^z = const.$ are equipotential surfaces, and find the potential function in each case.

CHAPTER 7

Green's Integral Theorems

7.1 Green's Theorems

Let $\phi(x, y, z)$ and $\psi(x, y, z)$ be scalar functions with continuous first and second partial derivatives. By Gauss's theorem applied to the vector $\phi \nabla\psi$, we have

$$\int_S \phi \nabla\psi . d\mathbf{S} = \int_V \nabla . (\phi \nabla\psi) \, dV$$

$$= \int_V \{\phi \nabla^2\psi + (\nabla\phi) . (\nabla\psi)\} \, dV. \tag{7.1}$$

But

$$\nabla\psi . d\mathbf{S} = \nabla\psi . \hat{\mathbf{n}} \, dS = \frac{\partial\psi}{\partial n} \, dS,$$

since $\nabla\psi . \hat{\mathbf{n}}$ is the directional derivative of ψ in the direction $\hat{\mathbf{n}}$. Therefore,

$$\int_V \{\phi \nabla^2\psi + (\nabla\phi) . (\nabla\psi)\} \, dV = \int_S \phi\frac{\partial\psi}{\partial n} \, dS. \tag{7.2}$$

This identity is known as *Green's first theorem*.

Interchanging the roles of ϕ and ψ gives

$$\int_V \{\psi \nabla^2\phi + (\nabla\psi) . (\nabla\phi)\} \, dV = \int_S \psi\frac{\partial\phi}{\partial n} \, dS.$$

On subtracting from (7.2),

$$\int_V (\phi \nabla^2\psi - \psi \nabla^2\phi) \, dV = \int_S \left(\phi\frac{\partial\psi}{\partial n} - \psi\frac{\partial\phi}{\partial n}\right) dS, \tag{7.3}$$

which is known as *Green's second theorem*.

In some applications, the above conditions are not satisfied because the normal derivatives $\partial\phi/\partial n$, $\partial\psi/\partial n$ are discontinuous at the boundary S. In this case, the theorems remain valid provided that $\partial/\partial n$ is taken to mean the rate of change along the outward normal direction, evaluated from the *inner* side of S.

7.2 Uniqueness Theorem for Poisson's Equation

As an application of Green's first theorem we shall prove a theorem on the uniqueness of the solution of Poisson's equation. In potential theory, it is often extremely useful to know what data, in addition to Poisson's equation (or, in particular, Laplace's equation), is sufficient to determine the potential uniquely in the region considered. For example, suppose that we are given that $\nabla^2\phi = 0$ everywhere in V, and that $\phi = 0$ everywhere on the bounding surface S. (These are the conditions satisfied by the potential in an earthed conductor with boundary S in electrostatics.) One solution of these conditions is evidently $\phi \equiv 0$ in V. Can we prove that this is the only solution?

We shall first prove the following result, which is a preliminary to a more general theorem. If the function $\phi(x,y,z)$ is continuous and possesses continuous first and second partial derivatives everywhere in V and on S, and if $\phi \equiv 0$ on S and $\nabla^2\phi \equiv 0$ in V, then $\phi \equiv 0$ in V.

Consider Green's first theorem in the case where ψ is put equal to ϕ,

$$\int_S \phi\frac{\partial\phi}{\partial n}\,dS = \int_V \{\phi\,\nabla^2\phi + (\nabla\phi)^2\}\,dV. \tag{7.4}$$

But $\phi \equiv 0$ on S, and so the integrand on the left is identically zero on S. Also, the first term in the integrand on the right vanishes since $\nabla^2\phi \equiv 0$ in V. Thus,

$$\int_V (\nabla\phi)^2\,dV = 0. \tag{7.5}$$

But $(\nabla\phi)^2$ is the square of the magnitude of $\nabla\phi$, and must satisfy $(\nabla\phi)^2 \geqslant 0$. Now, if $(\nabla\phi)^2 > 0$ at any particular point in V, then by continuity there is a neighbourhood of this point throughout which $(\nabla\phi)^2 > 0$, and the contribution to (7.5) from this neighbourhood must therefore be strictly positive. Since there can be no negative contributions to the integral, (7.5) would be contradicted. It follows that there can be no point in V at which $(\nabla\phi)^2 > 0$, and

$$(\nabla\phi)^2 \equiv 0$$

in V. Thus $\nabla\phi$ has zero magnitude, and we have

$$\nabla\phi \equiv 0. \tag{7.6}$$

This means that the partial derivatives of ϕ are identically zero, and so $\phi \equiv$ constant in V. Finally, since $\phi \equiv 0$ on S, the value of the constant must be zero, and

$$\phi \equiv 0$$

in V, as was to be proved.

A similar result applies if the boundary condition $\phi \equiv 0$ on S is replaced by the condition $\partial\phi/\partial n \equiv 0$, as occurs in some applications. Again, the surface integral (7.4) vanishes and, as before, we get $\phi \equiv$ constant in V. In this case, it does not follow that the constant is zero, and further information (such as the value of ϕ at one point) is necessary to determine its value.

A generalization of the above theorem is the following:

Uniqueness theorem. If ϕ is continuous and has continuous first and second partial derivatives in a region V and on its boundary S, and if $\phi = f$ on S, and $\nabla^2\phi = g$ in V, where f and g are given functions, then ϕ is unique.

The importance of this theorem is that it shows that the solution of Poisson's equation (with g written in place of $-\rho/\varepsilon_0$) is fully determined when the potential is specified on the boundary of the region considered. For example, in electrostatics, if the charge distribution is prescribed within an earthed conducting surface (i.e. one on which $\phi \equiv 0$), then ϕ is determined in the interior. From a mathematical point of view, this means that if, by any device, one finds a particular solution of Poisson's equation and the given boundary condition, then the physical problem of determining the interior potential is solved, since there can be no other solution than the one found.

The case $g = 0$ allows a simple and familiar physical interpretation. It may be shown that the temperature in a uniform body satisfies Laplace's equation if a steady state has been attained (i.e. the temperature at any point is not varying with time). The theorem thus expresses the intuitively evident fact that if the temperature is prescribed at all points of the surface, then the interior temperature is fully determined.

To prove the uniqueness theorem, suppose that $\phi = \phi_1(x,y,z)$ and $\phi = \phi_2(x,y,z)$ both satisfy the stated conditions. Then we shall show that $\phi_1 \equiv \phi_2$. We are given that

$$\phi_1 = f, \qquad \phi_2 = f, \qquad \text{on } S,$$

and

$$\nabla^2\phi_1 = g, \quad \nabla^2\phi_2 = g, \qquad \text{in } V.$$

Let Φ denote $\phi_1 - \phi_2$. By subtraction,

$$\Phi = \phi_1 - \phi_2 = f - f = 0 \qquad \text{on } S,$$

and

$$\nabla^2 \Phi = \nabla^2 \phi_1 - \nabla^2 \phi_2 = g - g = 0 \qquad \text{in } V.$$

Hence, Φ satisfies the conditions of the first result proved in this section, and so $\Phi \equiv 0$ in V. That is

$$\phi_1 - \phi_2 \equiv 0.$$

Thus, any two solutions are identical, and the theorem is proved. (Note that this theorem is not concerned with the *existence* of a solution, but only that there cannot be *more* than one solution.)

7.3   Green's Formula

If $\nabla^2 \phi = 0$ everywhere in V, then the value ϕ_P of ϕ at any interior P may be expressed explicitly in terms of ϕ and $\partial\phi/\partial n$ on the surface S. (The reader is reminded that values of ϕ and $\partial\phi/\partial n$ need not *both* be specified on S in order to make the solution of Laplace's equation in the interior unique. But the explicit formula for ϕ in terms of both boundary data is of importance in applications.)

To obtain the required formula for ϕ_P, we use Green's second theorem (7.3). Observe that on one side of (7.3) is a surface integral, and if we choose ϕ in (7.3) to be the ϕ in our problem, and ψ to be any definite

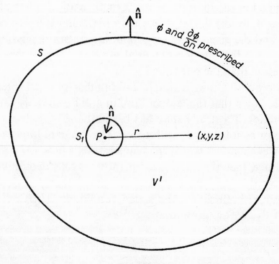

Fig. 7.1

function of x, y, z, then the surface integral involves no unknowns. Also, one term in the integrand of the volume integral in (7.3) vanishes, since $\nabla^2\phi = 0$ throughout V. In order to make the volume integral reduce, effectively, to ϕ_P, we choose ψ so that $\nabla^2\psi = 0$ except at P. Consider the choice

$$\psi(x, y, z) = \frac{1}{r} \equiv \frac{1}{\{(x-x_P)^2+(y-y_P)^2+(z-z_P)^2\}^{\frac{1}{2}}}, \quad (7.7)$$

where (x_P, y_P, z_P) are the coordinates of P, so that r is the distance of the point (x, y, z) from P. Since ψ is identically the potential of a point charge of magnitude $4\pi\varepsilon_0$ situated at P, it follows that $\nabla^2\psi = 0$ except at P.

To proceed further, we exclude from V the interior of a small spherical surface S_1, centred at P, because $\nabla^2\psi$ is not defined at P (Fig. 7.1). Let the radius of S_1 be r_1, and let V' denote the remaining part of V. Since $\nabla^2\phi = \nabla^2\psi = 0$ throughout V', by Green's theorem we have

$$\int_S \left\{\phi\frac{\partial}{\partial n}\left(\frac{1}{r}\right)-\frac{1}{r}\frac{\partial\phi}{\partial n}\right\} dS + \int_{S_1} \left\{\phi\frac{\partial}{\partial n}\left(\frac{1}{r}\right)-\frac{1}{r}\frac{\partial\phi}{\partial n}\right\} dS_1 = 0, \quad (7.8)$$

where in each case the normal direction points away from V'. On S_1,

$$\frac{\partial}{\partial n} = -\frac{\partial}{\partial r},$$

and so

$$\frac{\partial}{\partial n}\left(\frac{1}{r}\right) = \left|-\frac{\partial}{\partial r}\left(\frac{1}{r}\right)\right|_{r=r_1} = \frac{1}{r_1^2}.$$

The integral over S_1 therefore becomes

$$\int_{S_1} \left(\frac{1}{r_1^2}\phi+\frac{1}{r_1}\frac{\partial\phi}{\partial r}\right) dS_1. \quad (7.9)$$

We shall prove that, as $r_1 \to 0$,

$$\int_{S_1} \frac{1}{r_1^2}\phi\, dS_1 \to 4\pi\phi_P, \quad (7.10)$$

and

$$\int_{S_1} \frac{1}{r_1}\frac{\partial\phi}{\partial r}\, dS_1 \to 0, \quad (7.11)$$

so that in the limit, (7.9) tends to $4\pi\phi_P$.

For (7.10), by choosing r_1 sufficiently small, we can make $\phi-\phi_P$ as small as we please, since ϕ is continuous. Let ε denote the maximum value of $|\phi - \phi_P|$ on S_1, and note that $\varepsilon \to 0$ as $r_1 \to 0$. Consider

$$\int_{S_1} \frac{1}{r_1^2} \phi \, dS_1 - \int_{S_1} \frac{1}{r_1^2} \phi_P \, dS_1 = \frac{1}{r_1^2} \int_{S_1} (\phi - \phi_P) \, dS_1,$$

which tends to zero as $r_1 \to 0$ since the magnitude of the last expression does not exceed

$$\frac{1}{r_1^2} \varepsilon 4\pi r_1^2 = 4\pi\varepsilon.$$

The second integral on the left is

$$\frac{1}{r_1^2} \phi_P \int_{S_1} dS_1 = \frac{1}{r_1^2} \phi_P \, 4\pi r_1^2 = 4\pi\phi_P,$$

because ϕ_P is a constant, and so (7.10) is proved.

To prove (7.11), we have that $\partial\phi/\partial r$ is continuous, since it is assumed that ϕ has continuous first partial derivatives in V'. Therefore $|\partial\phi/\partial r| < c$ for some absolute constant c. It follows that the magnitude of the integral (7.11) does not exceed

$$\frac{1}{r_1} \int_{S_1} c \, dS_1 = \frac{c}{r_1} 4\pi r_1^2 = 4\pi c r_1,$$

which tends to zero as $r_1 \to 0$.

We have, therefore, that the value of (7.9) is $4\pi\phi_P$, and so by (7.8)

$$4\pi\phi_P = \int_{S} \left\{ \frac{1}{r} \frac{\partial\phi}{\partial n} - \phi \frac{\partial}{\partial n}\left(\frac{1}{r}\right) \right\} dS,$$

which is the required *Green's formula*.

EXERCISES

In the following exercises, it is to be assumed that all functions possess such properties of continuity and differentiability as necessary for the application of Green's theorems.

1.   Prove that if $\phi(x, y, z)$ satisfies the equation $\nabla . (K\nabla\phi) = -\rho/\varepsilon_0$ everywhere in a region V, where ρ and K are given point functions with $K > 0$, and if $\partial\phi/\partial n$ takes prescribed values on the boundary surface of V, then ϕ is determined to within an additive constant in V. (Assume that ϕ is continuous and has continuous derivatives up to second order. Use Green's first theorem.)

2. The *Legendre polynomial* $P_n(\mu)$, of degree n in μ, has the property that $r^n P_n(\cos\theta)$ satisfies Laplace's equation, r and θ being spherical polar coordinates and n being any positive integer or zero. By applying Green's second theorem to the functions $r^n P_n(\mu)$, $r^m P_m(\mu)$, where $\mu = \cos\theta$, over the unit sphere centred at the origin, show that for $m \neq n$,

$$\int_{-1}^{1} P_m P_n \, d\mu = 0.$$

3. The function $U(x, y, z, t)$ satisfies the *wave equation*

$$\nabla^2 U - \frac{1}{c^2}\frac{\partial^2 U}{\partial t^2} = 0,$$

(where c is a constant) everywhere in a region V bounded by a closed surface S. On S, U satisfies the boundary condition $aU + b\partial U/\partial n = 0$, where a and b are prescribed functions of position on S (and are not both zero at any point of S). Show that if U is of the form $\phi(x, y, z)\sin kt$, where k is a constant, then ϕ must satisfy the equations

$$\nabla^2\phi + \frac{k^2}{c^2}\phi = 0 \quad \text{in } V; \qquad a\phi + b\frac{\partial\phi}{\partial n} = 0 \quad \text{on } S.$$

By applying Green's second theorem, show that if $\phi_1(x, y, z)$ and $\phi_2(x, y, z)$ are two solutions of these equations, for distinct values of k, then $\int\limits_{V} \phi_1\phi_2 \, dV = 0$.

CHAPTER 8

Curl; Stokes's Theorem

8.1　The Curl of a Vector Point Function

The curl of a differentiable vector point function

$$\mathbf{F}(x, y, z) = F_x\mathbf{i} + F_y\mathbf{j} + F_z\mathbf{k}$$

has been defined in §6.1 as $\nabla \wedge \mathbf{F}$. This can be expressed also as a formal determinant;

$$\operatorname{curl} \mathbf{F} \equiv \nabla \wedge \mathbf{F} = \begin{vmatrix} \mathbf{i} & \mathbf{j} & \mathbf{k} \\ \dfrac{\partial}{\partial x} & \dfrac{\partial}{\partial y} & \dfrac{\partial}{\partial z} \\ F_x & F_y & F_z \end{vmatrix}$$

$$= \mathbf{i}\left(\frac{\partial F_z}{\partial y} - \frac{\partial F_y}{\partial z}\right) + \mathbf{j}\left(\frac{\partial F_x}{\partial z} - \frac{\partial F_z}{\partial x}\right) + \mathbf{k}\left(\frac{\partial F_y}{\partial x} - \frac{\partial F_x}{\partial y}\right) \qquad (8.1)$$

The significance of the curl of a vector field may be seen from the following example. Consider the motion of a rigid body which is rotating with angular velocity ω about an axis through a fixed point O. The velocity of any point P of the body is $\mathbf{v} = \omega \wedge \mathbf{r}$ (p. 24), where $\mathbf{r} = \overrightarrow{OP}$, and if $\mathbf{r} = x\mathbf{i} + y\mathbf{j} + z\mathbf{k}$, then $\mathbf{v}(x, y, z)$ is a vector point function. Now,

$$\omega \wedge \mathbf{r} = \begin{vmatrix} \mathbf{i} & \mathbf{j} & \mathbf{k} \\ \omega_x & \omega_y & \omega_z \\ x & y & z \end{vmatrix} = \mathbf{i}(\omega_y z - \omega_z y) + \mathbf{j}(\omega_z x - \omega_x z) + \mathbf{k}(\omega_x y - \omega_y x),$$

where $(\omega_x, \omega_y, \omega_z)$ are the rectangular components of ω. Therefore

$$\operatorname{curl} \mathbf{v} = \mathbf{i}\left\{\frac{\partial}{\partial y}(\omega_x y - \omega_y x) - \frac{\partial}{\partial z}(\omega_z x - \omega_x z)\right\} + \dots$$

$$= \mathbf{i}\{\omega_x + \omega_x\} + \mathbf{j}\{\omega_y + \omega_y\} + \mathbf{k}\{\omega_z + \omega_z\}$$

$$= 2\omega, \tag{8.2}$$

since $\omega_x, \omega_y, \omega_z$ are independent of x, y, z, and $\partial y/\partial y = 1$, $\partial x/\partial y = 0$, etc.

Thus, the curl of the velocity vector of a rigid body in rotation is equal to twice the angular velocity. This result remains valid when the body has translatory motion in addition to rotation. If the point O has velocity $\mathbf{v}_0$, and the motion relative to O is the same as before, then the velocity of P referred to fixed axes with O momentarily at the origin is $\mathbf{v} = \mathbf{v}_0 + \omega \wedge \mathbf{r}$. Since $\mathbf{v}_0$ is independent of x,y,z, we again get (8.2).

The curl of a vector field is a measure of its 'rotational' properties. In fact, the notation rot $\mathbf{F}$ is sometimes used in place of curl $\mathbf{F}$. In Fig. (8.1) is represented a typical vector field $\mathbf{F}$ for which curl $\mathbf{F} \neq 0$. Observe

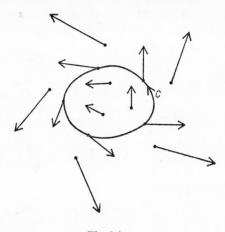

Fig. 8.1

from the diagram that in the particular case illustrated the tangential component of $\mathbf{F}$ to the closed curve C is positive at all points of C. Thus, the tangential line integral

$$\oint_C \mathbf{F} \cdot d\mathbf{r} > 0,$$

since the contribution from every differential element is positive. The line integral $\oint_C \mathbf{F} \cdot d\mathbf{r}$ is called the *circulation* of $\mathbf{F}$ around C. The rotational nature of a vector field may be indicated in two ways, (i) by the non-vanishing of its curl, and (ii) by the non-vanishing of its circulation around some closed curves. The equivalence of (i) and (ii) is proved formally and quantitatively in a theorem, known as Stokes's theorem, in later sections.

A vector field $\mathbf{F}$ such that curl $\mathbf{F} = 0$ everywhere in the region considered is called *irrotational*.

The following identities involving curl are valid. It is assumed that ϕ and $\mathbf{F}$ are continuous scalar and vector point functions, and that all relevant derivatives exist and are continuous:

$$\nabla \wedge (\phi \mathbf{F}) = \phi \nabla \wedge \mathbf{F} + \nabla \phi \wedge \mathbf{F}, \tag{8.3}$$

$$\nabla . (\nabla \wedge \mathbf{F}) = 0, \tag{8.4}$$

$$\nabla \wedge \nabla \phi = 0, \tag{8.5}$$

$$\nabla \wedge (\nabla \wedge \mathbf{F}) = \nabla (\nabla . \mathbf{F}) - \nabla^2 \mathbf{F}. \tag{8.6}$$

These identities can be remembered in the way described on p. 98. In particular, (8.4), (8.5), (8.6) are to be compared with the analogous vector and scalar identities $\mathbf{a} . (\mathbf{a} \wedge \mathbf{b}) = 0$, $\mathbf{a} \wedge a\mathbf{u} = 0$, $\mathbf{a} \wedge (\mathbf{a} \wedge \mathbf{b}) = \mathbf{a}(\mathbf{a} . \mathbf{b}) - a^2 \mathbf{b}$.

To prove (8.3), let $\mathbf{F} = F_x \mathbf{i} + F_y \mathbf{j} + F_z \mathbf{k}$. Then

$$\nabla \wedge (\phi \mathbf{F}) = \begin{vmatrix} \mathbf{i} & \mathbf{j} & \mathbf{k} \\ \dfrac{\partial}{\partial x} & \dfrac{\partial}{\partial y} & \dfrac{\partial}{\partial z} \\ \phi F_x & \phi F_y & \phi F_z \end{vmatrix}$$

$$= \mathbf{i} \left\{ \frac{\partial}{\partial y}(\phi F_z) - \frac{\partial}{\partial z}(\phi F_y) \right\} + \mathbf{j} \left\{ \frac{\partial}{\partial z}(\phi F_x) - \frac{\partial}{\partial x}(\phi F_z) \right\} + \mathbf{k} \left\{ \frac{\partial}{\partial x}(\phi F_y) - \frac{\partial}{\partial y}(\phi F_x) \right\}$$

$$= \mathbf{i} \left\{ \phi \frac{\partial F_z}{\partial y} + \frac{\partial \phi}{\partial y} F_z - \phi \frac{\partial F_y}{\partial z} - \frac{\partial \phi}{\partial z} F_y \right\}$$

$$+ \mathbf{j} \left\{ \phi \frac{\partial F_x}{\partial z} + \frac{\partial \phi}{\partial z} F_x - \phi \frac{\partial F_z}{\partial x} - \frac{\partial \phi}{\partial x} F_z \right\} + \mathbf{k} \left\{ \phi \frac{\partial F_y}{\partial x} + \frac{\partial \phi}{\partial x} F_y - \phi \frac{\partial F_x}{\partial y} - \frac{\partial \phi}{\partial y} F_x \right\}$$

$$= \phi \left\{ \mathbf{i} \left(\frac{\partial F_z}{\partial y} - \frac{\partial F_y}{\partial z} \right) + \mathbf{j} \left(\frac{\partial F_x}{\partial z} - \frac{\partial F_z}{\partial x} \right) + \mathbf{k} \left(\frac{\partial F_y}{\partial x} - \frac{\partial F_x}{\partial y} \right) \right\}$$

$$+ \mathbf{i} \left(\frac{\partial \phi}{\partial y} F_z - \frac{\partial \phi}{\partial z} F_y \right) + \mathbf{j} \left(\frac{\partial \phi}{\partial z} F_x - \frac{\partial \phi}{\partial x} F_z \right) + \mathbf{k} \left(\frac{\partial \phi}{\partial x} F_y - \frac{\partial \phi}{\partial y} F_x \right)$$

$$= \phi \begin{vmatrix} \mathbf{i} & \mathbf{j} & \mathbf{k} \\ \dfrac{\partial}{\partial x} & \dfrac{\partial}{\partial y} & \dfrac{\partial}{\partial z} \\ F_x & F_y & F_z \end{vmatrix} + \begin{vmatrix} \mathbf{i} & \mathbf{j} & \mathbf{k} \\ \dfrac{\partial \phi}{\partial x} & \dfrac{\partial \phi}{\partial y} & \dfrac{\partial \phi}{\partial z} \\ F_x & F_y & F_z \end{vmatrix}$$

$$= \phi \nabla \wedge \mathbf{F} + \nabla \phi \wedge \mathbf{F}.$$

To prove (8.4), we have

$$\nabla \cdot (\nabla \wedge \mathbf{F}) = \nabla \cdot \left\{ \mathbf{i} \left(\frac{\partial F_z}{\partial y} - \frac{\partial F_y}{\partial z} \right) + \mathbf{j} \left(\frac{\partial F_x}{\partial z} - \frac{\partial F_z}{\partial x} \right) + \mathbf{k} \left(\frac{\partial F_y}{\partial x} - \frac{\partial F_x}{\partial y} \right) \right\}$$

$$= \frac{\partial}{\partial x} \left(\frac{\partial F_z}{\partial y} - \frac{\partial F_y}{\partial z} \right) + \frac{\partial}{\partial y} \left(\frac{\partial F_x}{\partial z} - \frac{\partial F_z}{\partial x} \right) + \frac{\partial}{\partial z} \left(\frac{\partial F_y}{\partial x} - \frac{\partial F_x}{\partial y} \right)$$

$$= \frac{\partial^2 F_z}{\partial x \partial y} - \frac{\partial^2 F_y}{\partial x \partial z} + \frac{\partial^2 F_x}{\partial y \partial z} - \frac{\partial^2 F_z}{\partial y \partial x} + \frac{\partial^2 F_y}{\partial z \partial x} - \frac{\partial^2 F_x}{\partial z \partial y}$$

$$= 0,$$

since

$$\frac{\partial^2 F_z}{\partial x \partial y} = \frac{\partial^2 F_z}{\partial y \partial x},$$

etc., when both sides exist and are continuous. The reader should likewise verify (8.5) and (8.6), writing out both sides in full for the latter.

Example. Show that the curl of every *centrally symmetric* vector field is zero.

A vector field $\mathbf{F}$ is said to be *centrally symmetric* (or possess *spherical symmetry*) about the point O when it is of the form $\mathbf{F} = f(r)\hat{\mathbf{r}}$, where f is a scalar function of r, and $\mathbf{r} = x\mathbf{i} + y\mathbf{j} + z\mathbf{k}$. Thus, the magnitude of $\mathbf{F}$ depends only on the distance of the field point from O, and the direction of $\mathbf{F}$ is radially towards or away from O. Such a field is unchanged if rotated as a whole like a rigid body about O. We have

$$\text{curl } \mathbf{F} = \nabla \wedge \{ f(r) \hat{\mathbf{r}} \}$$

$$= \nabla \wedge \left\{ \frac{1}{r} f(r) \mathbf{r} \right\}$$

$$= \frac{1}{r} f(r) \nabla \wedge \mathbf{r} + \nabla \left\{ \frac{1}{r} f(r) \right\} \wedge \mathbf{r},$$

by (8.3). But

$$\nabla \wedge \mathbf{r} = \begin{vmatrix} \mathbf{i} & \mathbf{j} & \mathbf{k} \\ \dfrac{\partial}{\partial x} & \dfrac{\partial}{\partial y} & \dfrac{\partial}{\partial z} \\ x & y & z \end{vmatrix} = 0,$$

since all the derivatives $\partial z / \partial y$, $\partial y / \partial z$, etc. vanish. Also,

$$\nabla \left(\frac{1}{r} f \right) = \frac{d}{dr} \left(\frac{1}{r} f \right) \nabla r = \left(\frac{1}{r} \frac{df}{dr} - \frac{1}{r^2} f \right) \hat{\mathbf{r}},$$

by (4.17). Therefore,

$$\nabla \wedge (f\hat{\mathbf{r}}) = \left(\frac{1}{r}\frac{df}{dr} - \frac{1}{r^2}f\right)\hat{\mathbf{r}} \wedge \mathbf{r} = 0, \tag{8.7}$$

since $\hat{\mathbf{r}} \wedge \mathbf{r} = 0$.

8.2   Stokes's Theorem in the xy Plane

Definition. A *simple* closed curve in a plane is one with no double points (i.e. one which does not meet or cross itself).

Let S be a region of the xy plane enclosed by a simple closed curve C, such that any line parallel to the x axis or the y axis meets C in at most two points. If F_x and F_y are continuous functions with continuous first partial derivatives with respect to x and y (in S and on C) then

$$\iint_S \left(\frac{\partial F_y}{\partial x} - \frac{\partial F_x}{\partial y}\right) dx\,dy = \oint_C (F_x\,dx + F_y\,dy), \tag{8.8}$$

where C is to be described in the anticlockwise direction. This is Stokes's theorem in the xy plane, and the proof follows.

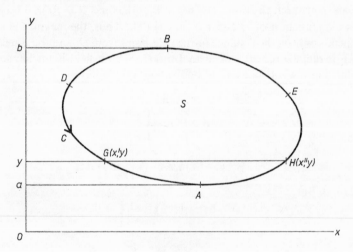

Fig. 8.2

In Fig. 8.2, a and b are the points where the tangents to C which are parallel to the x axis meet Oy, and A, B are the points of contact of these tangents with C. The points D and E are any two points on the segments of C between A and B, as shown, and are used simply to label these segments. The line GH, parallel to Ox, meets C in $G(x', y)$ and $H(x'', y)$, with $x' < x''$.

Consider

$$\iint\limits_{S} \frac{\partial F_y}{\partial x}\, dxdy = \int_a^b \left(\int_{x'}^{x''} \frac{\partial F_y}{\partial x}\, dx \right) dy = \int_a^b \left. |F_y| \right|_{(x',y)}^{(x'',y)} dy$$

$$= \int_a^b \{ F_y(x'', y) - F_y(x', y) \}\, dy.$$

Now, $F_y(x'', y)$ is the value of F_y at the point with ordinate y on the segment AEB of C. Therefore,

$$\int_a^b F_y(x'', y)\, dy = \int\limits_{AEB} F_y\, dy$$

and likewise

$$\int_a^b F_y(x', y)\, dy = \int\limits_{ADB} F_y\, dy = - \int\limits_{BDA} F_y\, dy.$$

On subtracting the last two results, we get

$$\iint\limits_{S} \frac{\partial F_y}{\partial x}\, dxdy = \left(\int\limits_{AEB} + \int\limits_{BDA} \right) F_y\, dy = \oint_C F_y\, dy, \qquad (8.9)$$

where C is described in the stated, anticlockwise, direction.

Next consider the second term in the double integral (8.8). To deal with this term in a similar way, we need to carry out the integration with respect to x first. In Fig. (8.3), lL and mM are tangents to C which are

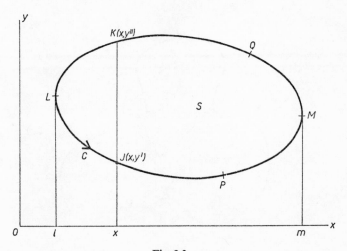

Fig. 8.3

parallel to Oy. The line JK parallel to Oy meets C in $J(x, y')$ and $K(x, y'')$, with $y' < y''$. The points P and Q label the segments of C between L and M. Now,

$$\iint_S \frac{\partial F_x}{\partial y} \, dx \, dy = \int_l^m \left(\int_{y'}^{y''} \frac{\partial F_x}{\partial y} \, dy \right) dx$$

$$= \int_l^m \left| F_x \right|_{(x,y')}^{(x,y'')} dx = \int_l^m \{ F_x(x, y'') - F_x(x, y') \} \, dx$$

But $F_x(x, y'')$ is the value of F_y at the point with abscissa x on the segment LQM, and so

$$\int_l^m F_x(x, y'') \, dx = \int_{LQM} F_x \, dx = - \int_{MQL} F_x \, dx,$$

and likewise

$$\int_l^m F_x(x, y') \, dx = \int_{LPM} F_x \, dx.$$

On subtracting, we get

$$\iint_S \frac{\partial F_x}{\partial y} \, dx \, dy = - \left(\int_{MQL} + \int_{LPM} \right) F_x \, dx = - \oint_C F_x \, dx. \qquad (8.10)$$

Finally, by subtracting (8.10) from (8.9), we obtain

$$\oint_C (F_x \, dx + F_y \, dy) = \iint_S \left(\frac{\partial F_y}{\partial x} - \frac{\partial F_x}{\partial y} \right) dx \, dy$$

as required.

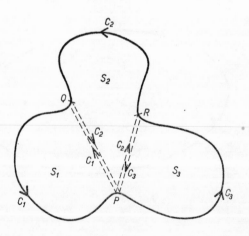

Fig. 8.4

The condition that C be met by a line parallel to the x axis or the y axis in at most two points can be relaxed if S can be divided into a finite number of parts, $S_1, S_2, \ldots, S_n$, whose boundaries $C_1, C_2, \ldots, C_n$ individually satisfy the condition. For example, in the case shown in Fig. 8.4, $n = 3$, and $S = S_1 + S_2 + S_3$. For each S_i $(i = 1, 2, \ldots, n)$, by Stokes's theorem

$$\iint_{S_i} \left(\frac{\partial F_y}{\partial x} - \frac{\partial F_x}{\partial y} \right) dxdy = \oint_{C_i} (F_x \, dx + F_y \, dy). \qquad (8.11)$$

On summation over i, the contributions to the line integrals from segments of paths such as PQ, QP, PR and RP, which separate the subregions S_i from one another, cancel in pairs because each segment is described in both directions. Therefore, the sum of the line integrals (8.11) reduces to a line integral around the boundary C of the whole region S, while the sum of the double integrals over S_i is a double integral over S. The result follows immediately.

8.3   The Positive Normal to an Open Surface

Let S be any open two-sided surface, and suppose that a definite sense of description is assigned to its boundary curve C (Fig. 8.5). Form any

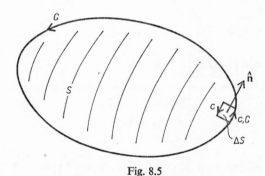

Fig. 8.5

element ΔS with normal $\hat{n}$ and boundary c, such that c and C have an arc in common. A sense of description is given to c by the direction in which the common arc is traversed, and if this is in the sense of a positive rotation about $\hat{n}$, then $\hat{n}$ is called the *positive normal* to the element ΔS. By moving $\hat{n}$ continuously over S, the positive normal at any point of S is (by definition) constructed.

An alternative statement of this relation between C and the positive normal $\hat{\mathbf{n}}$ to S is that C is *described positively* with respect to $\hat{\mathbf{n}}$.

8.4   Stokes's Theorem in Three Dimensions

Stokes's Theorem. Let S be an open (two-sided) surface whose projection on each of the xy, yz, zx planes is simple (p. 63). Let the equation of S be expressible in each of the forms $z = f(x, y)$, $x = g(y, z)$, $y = h(z, x)$, where f, g, h are continuous functions with continuous first partial derivatives. Then if $\mathbf{F} = F_x \mathbf{i} + F_y \mathbf{j} + F_z \mathbf{k}$ is continuous with continuous first partial derivatives (in S and on C),

$$\int_S \text{curl } \mathbf{F} . d\mathbf{S} = \oint_C \mathbf{F} . d\mathbf{r}, \tag{8.12}$$

where C is the boundary of S and is described positively with respect to $d\mathbf{S}$.

Note that if S is a region of the xy plane, and $\mathbf{F}$ is a two-dimensional vector in the plane, then (8.12) is identical to Stokes's theorem (8.8) in the xy plane.

Proof. The left hand side of (8.12) is

$$\int_S \text{curl } \mathbf{F} . d\mathbf{S} = \int_S \text{curl } (F_x \mathbf{i} + F_y \mathbf{j} + F_z \mathbf{k}) . \hat{\mathbf{n}} \, dS. \tag{8.13}$$

Consider the contribution from the term $\text{curl } (F_x \mathbf{i})$ in the integrand. We have

$$\text{curl } (F_x \mathbf{i}) = \begin{vmatrix} \mathbf{i} & \mathbf{j} & \mathbf{k} \\ \dfrac{\partial}{\partial x} & \dfrac{\partial}{\partial y} & \dfrac{\partial}{\partial z} \\ F_x & 0 & 0 \end{vmatrix} = \mathbf{j}\dfrac{\partial F_x}{\partial z} - \mathbf{k}\dfrac{\partial F_x}{\partial y}$$

and so

$$\text{curl } (F_x \mathbf{i}) . \hat{\mathbf{n}} \, dS = \left(\mathbf{j} . \hat{\mathbf{n}} \dfrac{\partial F_x}{\partial z} - \mathbf{k} . \hat{\mathbf{n}} \dfrac{\partial F_x}{\partial y} \right) dS. \tag{8.14}$$

Let $\hat{\mathbf{n}}$ be chosen so that it makes an acute angle with $\mathbf{k}$, as would be the case in Fig. 8.6. If we take dS to have a rectangular projection $dx\,dy$ on the xy plane, then

$$dS \mathbf{k} . \hat{\mathbf{n}} = dx\,dy, \tag{8.15}$$

which enables us to simplify the second term on the right in (8.14). For the other term, we shall express $\mathbf{j}.\hat{\mathbf{n}}$ in terms of $\mathbf{k}.\hat{\mathbf{n}}$, using the equation of the surface S. On S,

$$z - f(x, y) = 0,$$

and so by forming the gradient of $z - f(x, y)$ we find that $\hat{\mathbf{n}}$ is parallel to the vector

$$\left(-\frac{\partial f}{\partial x}, -\frac{\partial f}{\partial y}, 1\right).$$

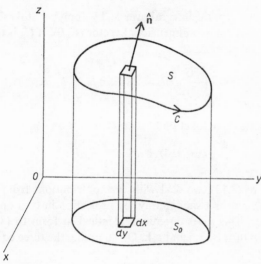

Fig. 8.6

Therefore, the ratio of the y component to the z component of $\hat{\mathbf{n}}$ is

$$\mathbf{j}.\hat{\mathbf{n}} : \mathbf{k}.\hat{\mathbf{n}} = -\frac{\partial f}{\partial y} : 1,$$

which gives

$$\mathbf{j}.\hat{\mathbf{n}} = -\frac{\partial f}{\partial y}\mathbf{k}.\hat{\mathbf{n}}. \tag{8.16}$$

On substituting this value for $\mathbf{j}.\hat{\mathbf{n}}$ into (8.14), we get by (8.15),

$$\text{curl}(F_x\mathbf{i}).\hat{\mathbf{n}}\,dS = -\left(\frac{\partial F_x}{\partial y} + \frac{\partial F_x}{\partial z}\frac{\partial f}{\partial y}\right)dx\,dy. \tag{8.17}$$

The terms in brackets may be given a simple interpretation using the chain rule of partial differentiation. Let $G(x, y)$ denote F_x on the surface S, that is

$$F_x(x, y, z) = F_x(x, y, f(x, y)) \equiv G(x, y).$$

I

Then

$$\frac{\partial G}{\partial y} = \frac{\partial F_x}{\partial y} + \frac{\partial F_x}{\partial z}\frac{\partial f}{\partial y}. \qquad (8.18)$$

Thus, if S_0 is the projection of S on the xy plane, we obtain on integrating (8.17)

$$\int_S \mathrm{curl}(F_x\mathbf{i}).\,\hat{\mathbf{n}}\,dS = -\iint_{S_0} \frac{\partial G}{\partial y}\,dxdy. \qquad (8.19)$$

Finally, we transform the integral over S_0 by applying Stokes's theorem in the xy plane to the two-dimensional vector $(G, 0)$. If C_0 is the projection of C on the plane, then

$$-\iint_{S_0} \frac{\partial G}{\partial y}\,dxdy = \oint_{C_0} G\,dx = \oint_C F_x\,dx,$$

because F_x is the same function of x on C as is G on C_0. Therefore,

$$\int_S \mathrm{curl}(F_x\mathbf{i}).\,\hat{\mathbf{n}}\,dS = \oint_C F_x\,dx. \qquad (8.20)$$

Returning to (8.13), we deal with the contributions from the other terms on the right in a similar way, by projection in turn on to the yz and zx planes. This gives equations identical in form to (8.20), with $x, \mathbf{i}$ replaced in turn by $y, \mathbf{j}$ and $z, \mathbf{k}$. On summing the three equations so found, we get

$$\int_S \mathrm{curl}\,\mathbf{F}.\,d\mathbf{S} = \int_S \mathrm{curl}(F_x\mathbf{i}+F_y\mathbf{j}+F_z\mathbf{k}).\,\hat{\mathbf{n}}\,dS$$

$$= \oint_C (F_x\,dx + F_y\,dy + F_z\,dz) = \oint_C \mathbf{F}.\,d\mathbf{r},$$

as required.

Sometimes we need to apply Stokes's theorem to more general surfaces than in the above statement of the theorem. If the surface can be divided into a finite number of parts, each satisfying the stated conditions, then the theorem is again valid. The proof is akin to that on p. 127 relating to Stokes's theorem in the xy plane.

Another important case in practice is that where the surface is *non-simply connected*.

Definition. A region of space R is said to be *simply connected* if every closed curve in R can be shrunk continuously to a point without leaving R.

For example, the interior of a sphere and the surface of a sphere are each simply connected regions; so is a disc. But neither the interior of a torus nor its surface are simply connected, as we see from Fig. 8.7,

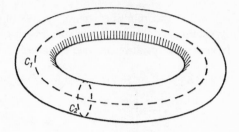

Fig. 8.7

because the curves C_1 and C_2 cannot be shrunk to zero without leaving the respective regions. In a plane, an annulus (the region between two concentric circles) is an example of a non-simply connected region. In physical problems, non-simply connected surfaces often arise as boundaries of regions following the exclusion of points at which field vectors are discontinuous.

Fig. 8.8. shows how to deal with a typical case, in which the surface S is bounded by the closed curves C_1, C_2 and C_3. 'Cuts' along AB and DE have been made in order to make S simply connected, and so the contour C relevant to Stokes's theorem is as indicated by arrows. Since the contributions to the integral around C from the segments AB and DE are cancelled when the segments are traversed in the opposite directions, we may regard C as consisting of the three parts C_1, C_2, C_3, described in

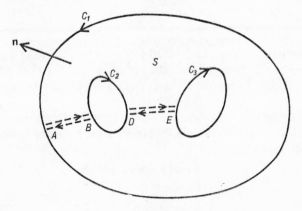

Fig. 8.8

the direction of the arrows. Any surface which becomes simply connected when a finite number of cuts are introduced can be dealt with in this way.

Example (i). Use Stokes's theorem to calculate the flux of curl $\mathbf{F}$, where $\mathbf{F} = xz\mathbf{i} - yz\mathbf{j} + 2xy\mathbf{k}$, through that part of the surface $4x^2 + 9y^2 + z^2 = 10$ for which $y \geqslant 1$. Verify the result by another method.

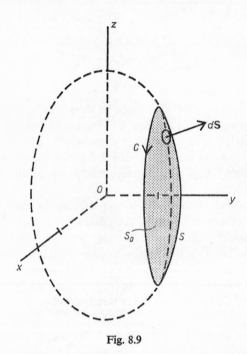

Fig. 8.9

We note that if any plane parallel to a coordinate plane $x = const.$, $y = const.$ or $z = const.$ meets the surface $4x^2 + 9y^2 + z^2 = 10$, it does so in an ellipse. Hence the given surface, S, is part of an ellipsoid (Fig. 8.9).

Take $d\mathbf{S}$ to be in the direction of the outward drawn normal to the ellipsoid. Then C is to be described in the sense indicated in the Figure, and by Stokes's theorem

$$\int_S \operatorname{curl} \mathbf{F} . d\mathbf{S} = \oint_C \mathbf{F} . d\mathbf{r}.$$

On C,

$$d\mathbf{r} = dx\,\mathbf{i} + dz\,\mathbf{k}$$

and

$$\mathbf{F}.d\mathbf{r} = xz\,dx + 2xy\,dz = xz\,dx + 2x\,dz,$$

since $y = 1$. Parametrize C ($4x^2 + z^2 = 1$, $y = 1$) by putting

$$2x = \cos t, \quad z = -\sin t, \quad 0 \leqslant t \leqslant 2\pi,$$

where the minus sign is appropriate because z decreases initially as t increases from zero. Therefore,

$$dx = -\tfrac{1}{2}\sin t\,dt, \quad dz = -\cos t\,dt,$$

and so for the required flux (measured outwards) we have

$$\int_S \operatorname{curl}\mathbf{F}.d\mathbf{S} = \oint_C (xz\,dx + 2x\,dz)$$

$$= \int_0^{2\pi} \{-\tfrac{1}{2}\cos t\sin t(-\tfrac{1}{2}\sin t\,dt) + \cos t(-\cos t\,dt)\}$$

$$= \int_0^{2\pi} (\tfrac{1}{4}\sin^2 t\cos t - \cos^2 t)\,dt = -\pi,$$

on performing the integration.

The result may be verified by forming curl $\mathbf{F}$, which is found to be $(2x+y)\mathbf{i} + (x-2y)\mathbf{j}$, and calculating the flux integral over S directly by one of the methods in §3.9. Or, we may use Gauss's theorem, as in the example on p. 105. The latter method is basically simpler, because div curl $\equiv 0$, and so if S_0 is the ellipse formed by the intersection of S with the plane $y = 1$,

$$\int_{S+S_0} \operatorname{curl}\mathbf{F}.d\mathbf{S} = \int_V \operatorname{div}\operatorname{curl}\mathbf{F}\,dV = 0,$$

where V is the volume enclosed by S and S_0, and the normal on S_0 is in the direction of $-\mathbf{j}$. Therefore,

$$\int_S \operatorname{curl}\mathbf{F}.d\mathbf{S} = \iint_{S_0} \operatorname{curl}\mathbf{F}.\mathbf{j}\,dx\,dz$$

$$= \iint_{S_0} (x-2)\,dx\,dz$$

$$= \int_{-\frac{1}{2}}^{\frac{1}{2}} \int_{-\sqrt{(1-4x^2)}}^{\sqrt{(1-4x^2)}} (x-2)\,dx\,dz$$

$$= -\pi,$$

as before.

In the following examples C and S have the same meaning as in Stokes's theorem.

Example (ii). Prove the identity

$$\oint_C \phi \, \nabla\psi . d\mathbf{r} = \int_S (\nabla\phi \wedge \nabla\psi) . d\mathbf{S},$$

where ϕ and ψ are continuous scalar functions with continuous first and second partial derivatives.

By Stokes's theorem,

$$\oint_C \phi \, \nabla\psi . d\mathbf{r} = \int_S \nabla \wedge (\phi \, \nabla\psi) . d\mathbf{S} = \int_S (\phi\nabla \wedge \nabla\psi + \nabla\phi \wedge \nabla\psi) . d\mathbf{S}$$

$$= \int_S (\nabla\phi \wedge \nabla\psi) . d\mathbf{S},$$

where we have used (8.3), and the identity $\nabla \wedge \nabla\psi = 0$.

Example (iii). Prove that

$$\oint_C r^2 \, d\mathbf{r} = -2 \int_S \mathbf{r} \wedge d\mathbf{S},$$

where $\mathbf{r} = x\mathbf{i} + y\mathbf{j} + z\mathbf{k}$.

To get the line integral into a form to which Stokes's theorem is applicable, we use a device employed in a previous example (p. 106). Let $\hat{\mathbf{a}}$ be an arbitrary constant unit vector. Then

$$\hat{\mathbf{a}} . \oint_C r^2 \, d\mathbf{r} = \oint_C r^2\hat{\mathbf{a}} . d\mathbf{r} = \int_S (\nabla \wedge r^2\hat{\mathbf{a}}) . d\mathbf{S} = \int_S (r^2 \nabla \wedge \hat{\mathbf{a}} + \nabla r^2 \wedge \hat{\mathbf{a}}) . d\mathbf{S}.$$

But $\nabla \wedge \hat{\mathbf{a}} = 0$, since $\hat{\mathbf{a}}$ is a constant vector, and

$$\nabla r^2 = 2r \, \nabla r = 2r\hat{\mathbf{r}} = 2\mathbf{r}.$$

Therefore,

$$\hat{\mathbf{a}} . \oint_C r^2 \, d\mathbf{r} = 2 \int_S (\mathbf{r} \wedge \hat{\mathbf{a}}) . d\mathbf{S}$$

$$= 2 \int_S (\mathbf{r} \wedge \hat{\mathbf{a}}) . \hat{\mathbf{n}} \, dS = -2 \int_S \hat{\mathbf{a}} . (\mathbf{r} \wedge \hat{\mathbf{n}}) \, dS$$

$$= -2\hat{\mathbf{a}} . \int_S \mathbf{r} \wedge d\mathbf{S},$$

where we have used a standard property of scalar triple products. Thus, since $\hat{\mathbf{a}}$ is arbitrary,

$$\oint_C r^2 \, d\mathbf{r} = -2 \int_S \mathbf{r} \wedge d\mathbf{S}.$$

8.5   Alternative Definition of Curl

We obtain an integral expression for curl, corresponding to that given for divergence in §6.4. Let P be any point in a region in which there is a vector field $\mathbf{F}$, such that curl $\mathbf{F}$ is continuous. Let ΔS be a plane elementary surface which contains the point P and is bounded by a curve C (Fig. 8.10). By Stokes's theorem,

$$\int_{\Delta S} \text{curl } \mathbf{F} \,.\, d\mathbf{S} = \int_{\Delta S} \text{curl } \mathbf{F} \,.\, \hat{\mathbf{n}} \, dS = \oint_{C} \mathbf{F} \,.\, d\mathbf{r}, \qquad (8.21)$$

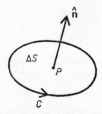

Fig. 8.10

where C is described positively with respect to the unit normal $\hat{\mathbf{n}}$ to ΔS.

Since curl $\mathbf{F}$ is continuous, its value at any point $Q(x, y, z)$ on ΔS may be written

$$\text{curl } \mathbf{F} = (\text{curl } \mathbf{F})_P + \boldsymbol{\varepsilon}(x, y, z),$$

where $\boldsymbol{\varepsilon} \to 0$ as $Q \to P$. Therefore,

$$\int_{\Delta S} \text{curl } \mathbf{F} \,.\, \hat{\mathbf{n}} \, dS = \int_{\Delta S} \{(\text{curl } \mathbf{F})_P + \boldsymbol{\varepsilon}\} \,.\, \hat{\mathbf{n}} \, dS$$

$$= (\text{curl } \mathbf{F})_P \,.\, \hat{\mathbf{n}} \, \Delta S + \int_{\Delta S} \boldsymbol{\varepsilon} \,.\, \hat{\mathbf{n}} \, dS.$$

Thus, by (8.21), we get on dividing by ΔS,

$$(\text{curl } \mathbf{F})_P \,.\, \hat{\mathbf{n}} = \frac{1}{\Delta S} \oint_{C} \mathbf{F} \,.\, d\mathbf{r} - \frac{1}{\Delta S} \int_{\Delta S} \boldsymbol{\varepsilon} \,.\, \hat{\mathbf{n}} \, dS.$$

By an argument exactly like that used for a similar integral in §6.4, it is easily shown that the second term on the right tends to zero, as $\Delta S \to 0$. Hence,

$$(\text{curl } \mathbf{F})_P . \hat{\mathbf{n}} = \lim_{\Delta S \to 0} \frac{1}{\Delta S} \oint_C \mathbf{F} . d\mathbf{r}. \qquad (8.22)$$

The direction of $\hat{\mathbf{n}}$ in this equation is arbitrary since the element ΔS may have any orientation. Thus, at a point P, the component of curl $\mathbf{F}$ in any direction $\hat{\mathbf{n}}$ is the 'circulation per unit area' around a plane element with normal $\hat{\mathbf{n}}$ at P. Equation (8.22) may be regarded as an alternative to the previous definition of curl $\mathbf{F}$.

Since $\hat{\mathbf{n}}$ has constant magnitude, the maximum value in (8.22) is obtained when $\hat{\mathbf{n}}$ points in the direction of curl $\mathbf{F}$. We may say, therefore, that the direction of curl $\mathbf{F}$ is defined as normal to ΔS when the latter is oriented so that the circulation is a maximum, measured in the positive sense around the boundary. With this orientation, the circulation per unit area is equal to the magnitude of curl $\mathbf{F}$, since we then have

$$(\text{curl } \mathbf{F})_P . \hat{\mathbf{n}} = |(\text{curl } \mathbf{F})_P|.$$

Because the circulation around the boundary of a surface element is independent of the choice of coordinate axes, it follows from (8.22) that the curl of a vector $\mathbf{F}$, as defined in 8.1, is *invariant* with respect to transformations of the rectangular cartesian coordinates.

EXERCISES

1. Verify the following identities, where $\mathbf{A}$ and $\mathbf{B}$ are differentiable point functions:

    (i) $\nabla . (\mathbf{A} \wedge \mathbf{B}) = \mathbf{B} . (\nabla \wedge \mathbf{A}) - \mathbf{A} . (\nabla \wedge \mathbf{B})$,

    (ii) $\mathbf{A} \wedge (\nabla \wedge \mathbf{A}) = \frac{1}{2}\nabla A^2 - (\mathbf{A} . \nabla)\mathbf{A}$,

    (iii) $\nabla(\mathbf{A} . \mathbf{B}) = (\mathbf{A} . \nabla)\mathbf{B} + (\mathbf{B} . \nabla)\mathbf{A} + \mathbf{A} \wedge (\nabla \wedge \mathbf{B}) + \mathbf{B} \wedge (\nabla \wedge \mathbf{A})$,

    (iv) $\nabla \wedge (\mathbf{A} \wedge \mathbf{B}) = (\nabla . \mathbf{B})\mathbf{A} - (\nabla . \mathbf{A})\mathbf{B} + (\mathbf{B} . \nabla)\mathbf{A} - (\mathbf{A} . \nabla)\mathbf{B}$.

2. Show that the vector field $\mathbf{F} = 2xyz\mathbf{i} + x^2z\mathbf{j} + x^2y\mathbf{k}$ is irrotational. Find a scalar point function ϕ such that $\mathbf{F} = \text{grad } \phi$.

3. Use Stokes's theorem to evaluate $\int \text{curl } \mathbf{F} . d\mathbf{S}$ over the open hemispherical surface $x^2 + y^2 + z^2 = a^2$, $z > 0$, where $\mathbf{F} = y\mathbf{i} + zx\mathbf{j} + y\mathbf{k}$. Compare the result with your answer to exercise 8, Chapter 6.

4. Prove that if $\mathbf{a}$ is constant and $\mathbf{r} = x\mathbf{i} + y\mathbf{j} + z\mathbf{k}$, then $\text{curl } r\mathbf{a} = \hat{\mathbf{r}} \wedge \mathbf{a}$. Hence show by use of Stokes's theorem that if S is an open surface bounded by the curve C, then $\int_S \mathbf{r} \wedge d\mathbf{S} = - \oint_C r \, d\mathbf{r}$, where C is described positively with respect to $d\mathbf{S}$.

5. If $\phi = \phi(u,v)$, $u = u(x,y,z)$ and $v = v(x,y,z)$ are differentiable functions and u, v possess continuous second partial derivatives, show that

$$\nabla . \{\phi(u,v)\nabla u \wedge \nabla v\} = 0$$

6. Prove that $\int \mathbf{r} \wedge d\mathbf{S} = 0$ over any closed surface S, where $\mathbf{r}$ denotes $x\mathbf{i} + y\mathbf{j} + z\mathbf{k}$.

7. Let $\phi, \mathbf{A}$ be differentiable point functions and let $\mathbf{A}$ possess continuous second partial derivatives. Prove that if $\operatorname{div} \mathbf{A} = 0$, and S, C have the same meanings as in Stokes's theorem, then

$$\int_S \{\phi \nabla^2 A + (\operatorname{curl} \mathbf{A}) \wedge \operatorname{grad} \phi\} . d\mathbf{S} = - \oint_C \phi \operatorname{curl} \mathbf{A} . d\mathbf{r}$$

8. If the vector function $\mathbf{F}$ is continuous and has continuous first partial derivatives, and if $\mathbf{F}$ is normal to a closed surface S at each point of S, show that

$$\int \operatorname{curl} \mathbf{F} \, dV = 0$$

over the volume enclosed by S. (Hint: Consider $\int_S \mathbf{F} \wedge d\mathbf{S}$.)

9. The flow of electric charge in space is described by the *current density vector* $\mathbf{j}$, whose direction is that of the mean flow at each point and whose magnitude is equal to the rate of flow per unit area across a plane element of surface normal to the flow. According to *Ampere's circuital relation*, if the current flow is steady (i.e. $\partial \mathbf{j}/\partial t = 0$), it gives rise to a magnetic field $\mathbf{H}$ which satisfies, in S.I. units,

$$\oint_C \mathbf{H} . d\mathbf{r} = \int_S \mathbf{j} . d\mathbf{S},$$

where S and C have the same meanings as in Stokes's theorem, and are otherwise arbitrary. Deduce Maxwell's field equation, for steady currents,

$$\operatorname{curl} \mathbf{H} = \mathbf{j}.$$

10. If S is a closed surface enclosing the volume region V, prove that

$$\int_S (\mathbf{F} \wedge \operatorname{grad} \phi) . d\mathbf{S} = \int_V (\operatorname{curl} \mathbf{F}) . \operatorname{grad} \phi \, dV$$

where $\mathbf{F}$ and ϕ are differentiable point functions, and ϕ possesses continuous second partial derivatives. Deduce that if V is bounded by a level surface of ϕ, then

$$\int_V (\operatorname{curl} \mathbf{F}) . \operatorname{grad} \phi \, dV = 0.$$

CHAPTER 9

Scalar and Vector Potentials

9.1 The Scalar Potential

Since curl grad $\phi = 0$ for every scalar point function ϕ (assuming that ϕ is continuous and has continuous partial derivatives up to second order), it follows that a *necessary* condition for a vector $\mathbf{F}$ to be expressible as (minus) the gradient of a scalar potential is that curl $\mathbf{F} = 0$. Conversely, one might ask: Does a scalar potential exist for *every* irrotational field? An answer is given in the following theorem.

Theorem. If $\mathbf{F}$ is continuous, with continuous first partial derivatives, and curl $\mathbf{F} = 0$ everywhere in a *simply connected* region R, then there exists a single valued scalar function ϕ such that $\mathbf{F} = -\operatorname{grad} \phi$ everywhere in R.

The proof of this result is quite simple. Let C be any closed curve in R. Because R is simply connected, C could shrink continuously to zero without leaving the region, and if it did so it would trace out some surface, which we call S. (There are, of course, an infinity of possible choices for this surface.) Therefore, the curve C, in its original position, is the boundary of an open surface S in the region, and so by Stokes's theorem

$$\oint_C \mathbf{F} . d\mathbf{r} = \int_S \operatorname{curl} \mathbf{F} . d\mathbf{S} = 0,$$

since curl $\mathbf{F} = 0$. But, by the theorem on p. 81, this is the condition for $\mathbf{F}$ to be expressible as the gradient of a single valued scalar function in R, and the result follows.

An example of a situation involving a non-simply connected region occurs in electromagnetic theory. When a steady electric current I flows along a straight infinite wire *in vacuo*, it gives rise to a magnetic field, for which the magnetic induction vector **B** is as shown in Fig. 9.1. The vector **B** at P is tangential to the circle (through P) whose plane is normal to the wire and whose centre lies on the wire, and **B** is directed in the sense of a positive rotation about the direction of the current. The magnitude of **B**

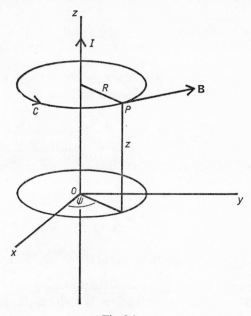

Fig. 9.1

is $\mu_0 I/2\pi R$, where μ_0 is a certain constant (the *permeability of free space*) and R is the distance from P to the wire. In cylindrical polar coordinates, with z axis taken along the wire, we therefore have

$$\mathbf{B} = \frac{\mu_0 I}{2\pi R}\hat{\psi}, \qquad (R \neq 0).$$

Consider curl **B**. An expression for the curl of a vector in cylindrical polar coordinates is derived in Chapter 10 (see p. 151). Using it, we find

$$\text{curl } \mathbf{B} = \frac{\mu_0 I}{2\pi}\begin{vmatrix} \hat{R} & R\hat{\psi} & \hat{z} \\ \dfrac{\partial}{\partial R} & \dfrac{\partial}{\partial \psi} & \dfrac{\partial}{\partial z} \\ 0 & 1 & 0 \end{vmatrix} = 0, \qquad (R \neq 0). \qquad (9.1)$$

Therefore, curl **B** vanishes everywhere in the non-simply connected region consisting of all space excluding the z axis. Now let us calculate the tangential line integral of $\mathbf{B}$ around the circle C in the Fig. 9.1. Since, on C, $d\mathbf{r} = R\,d\psi\,\hat{\psi}$ we have

$$\oint_{C} \mathbf{B}\,.\,d\mathbf{r} = \frac{\mu_0 I}{2\pi} \oint_{C} \frac{1}{R}\hat{\psi}\,.\,R\,d\psi\,\hat{\psi} = \frac{\mu_0 I}{2\pi} \int_{0}^{2\pi} d\psi = \mu_0 I \qquad (9.2)$$

Thus, (9.1) does not imply the vanishing of the tangential line integral because C could not shrink to zero without leaving the region in which (9.1) applies.

It follows from (9.2) that $\mathbf{B}$ is not expressible as the gradient of a single valued scalar function ϕ. Now, consider the scalar

$$\Omega = -\frac{\mu_0 I}{2\pi}\psi. \qquad (9.3)$$

By the formula obtained in the next chapter for the gradient operator in cylindrical polar coordinates (10.10), we have

$$\operatorname{grad}\Omega = \frac{1}{R}\frac{\partial}{\partial\psi}\left(-\frac{\mu_0 I}{2\pi}\psi\right)\hat{\psi} = -\frac{\mu_0 I}{2\pi R}\hat{\psi},$$

and so

$$\mathbf{B} = -\operatorname{grad}\Omega.$$

Thus, there exists a scalar potential Ω for the field vector $\mathbf{B}$, but by (9.3) Ω is *multivalued*, because the angle ψ is multivalued. In a complete positive circuit around the current, ψ increases by 2π, and so Ω decreases by $\mu_0 I$.

Exercise. Prove Ampère's circuital relation, which says that for a single positive circuit around the current, along a closed path C' of arbitrary shape,

$$\oint_{C'} \mathbf{B}\,.\,d\mathbf{r} = \mu_0 I.$$

(Use (9.2), and apply Stokes's theorem over an open surface bounded by C and C'.)

9.2   The Vector Potential

When a volume distribution of electric charge is in motion, it forms a current, and so gives rise to a magnetic field. But in this case, it may be shown that curl $\mathbf{B} \neq 0$ in the region occupied by charge. For this reason, even a multivalued scalar potential cannot be defined. It so happens, however, that in all cases the equation

$$\text{div}\,\mathbf{B} = 0 \tag{9.4}$$

is satisfied. Since div curl $\equiv 0$, this suggests the possibility of expressing $\mathbf{B}$ as the curl of another vector $\mathbf{A}$, known as the *vector potential* of $\mathbf{B}$. The reason for introducing the vector potential is that frequently the field equations satisfied by $\mathbf{A}$ are simpler to handle than those for $\mathbf{B}$.

For a given vector $\mathbf{B}$, the equation

$$\mathbf{B} = \text{curl}\,\mathbf{A} \tag{9.5}$$

cannot determine $\mathbf{A}$ uniquely, since if f is any scalar function, then

$$\text{curl}\,\mathbf{A} = \text{curl}\,(\mathbf{A} + \text{grad}\,f)$$

because curl grad $\equiv 0$. That is, if we add the gradient of an arbitrary scalar to any *one* solution of (9.5) for $\mathbf{A}$, we obtain another solution. The vector potential is made unique by specifying also the divergence of $\mathbf{A}$, together with certain conditions on $\mathbf{A}$ at the boundary of the region of interest. For example, in steady state problems (i.e. where fields are not time dependent) one imposes the condition that the divergence of $\mathbf{A}$ should vanish.

To discuss the existence of a vector potential in a region of arbitrary shape is beyond the scope of this book. The following theorem deals with the case of a rectangular region, and can be extended to the case where the region is the whole of space.

Theorem. If div $\mathbf{B} = 0$ everywhere in the rectangular region R

$$(x_0 \leqslant x \leqslant x_1, \quad y_0 \leqslant y \leqslant y_1, \quad z_0 \leqslant z \leqslant z_1),$$

then there exists a vector function $\mathbf{A}$ such that

$$\text{curl}\,\mathbf{A} = \mathbf{B}, \qquad \text{div}\,\mathbf{A} = g, \tag{9.6}$$

everywhere in R, where g is any prescribed scalar function. (It is assumed that g and $\mathbf{B}$ are continuous, and that $\mathbf{B}$ has continuous first partial derivatives.)

The method of proof is first to find a vector function $\mathbf{A_0}$ which satisfies the first of conditions (9.6), but not necessarily the second condition. Since, as we know, such $\mathbf{A_0}$ cannot be unique if it exists at all, it is reasonable to look for a vector $\mathbf{A_0}$ of a particularly simple form. Let us try putting (c.f. V.C.A. Ferraro, *Electromagnetic Theory* (Athlone Press, 1956))

$$\mathbf{A_0} = (\alpha, \beta, 0)$$

where α, β are functions of x, y and z. By direct calculation, we find

$$\text{curl } \mathbf{A}_0 = -\frac{\partial \beta}{\partial z}\mathbf{i} + \frac{\partial \alpha}{\partial z}\mathbf{j} + \left(\frac{\partial \beta}{\partial x} - \frac{\partial \alpha}{\partial y}\right)\mathbf{k},$$

and this is equal to $\mathbf{B} = B_x\mathbf{i} + B_y\mathbf{j} + B_z\mathbf{k}$ if

$$-\frac{\partial \beta}{\partial z} = B_x, \qquad \frac{\partial \alpha}{\partial z} = B_y, \qquad \frac{\partial \beta}{\partial x} - \frac{\partial \alpha}{\partial y} = B_z. \tag{9.7}$$

Integrating the first of these equations with respect to z, with x and y fixed, gives

$$\beta(x, y, z) = -\int_{z_0}^{z} B_x \, dz + b(x, y), \tag{9.8}$$

where b is an arbitrary function of integration. Similarly, from the second of (9.7) we get

$$\alpha(x, y, z) = \int_{z_0}^{z} B_y \, dz + a(x, y), \tag{9.9}$$

where a is arbitrary. Substituting the last two results into the third of (9.7), gives (by differentiation under the integral signs)

$$-\int_{z_0}^{z} \left(\frac{\partial B_x}{\partial x} + \frac{\partial B_y}{\partial y}\right) dz + \frac{\partial b}{\partial x} - \frac{\partial a}{\partial y} = B_z. \tag{9.10}$$

But $\text{div } \mathbf{B} = 0$, and so the integral term is equal to

$$\int_{z_0}^{z} \frac{\partial B_z}{\partial z} \, dz = B_z(x, y, z) - B_z(x, y, z_0),$$

and (9.10) therefore becomes

$$\frac{\partial b}{\partial x} - \frac{\partial a}{\partial y} = B_z(x, y, z_0). \tag{9.11}$$

This is satisfied if we choose, for example,

$$a = 0, \qquad b = \int_{x_0}^{x} B_z(x, y, z_0) \, dx,$$

where y is kept fixed in the integration. Thus, we have shown that it is possible to satisfy all the conditions (9.7) on α and β in order that $\mathbf{A}_0 = (\alpha, \beta, 0)$ should satisfy $\text{curl } \mathbf{A}_0 = \mathbf{B}$.

Next, we have to deal with the second of conditions (9.6). Put $\mathbf{A} = \mathbf{A}_0 + \text{grad } \psi$, for a certain scalar function ψ. Then

$$\text{curl } \mathbf{A} = \text{curl } (\mathbf{A}_0 + \text{grad } \psi) = \text{curl } \mathbf{A}_0 = \mathbf{B},$$

and

$$\operatorname{div} A = \operatorname{div}(A_0 + \operatorname{grad} \psi) = \operatorname{div} A_0 + \nabla^2 \psi = g,$$

provided that

$$\nabla^2 \psi = g - \operatorname{div} A_0, \qquad (9.12)$$

where the right hand side of the last equation is a definite scalar function. Since (9.12) is Poisson's equation for ψ, a solution can be written down as a volume integral over R in the form (6.34) (with ϕ replaced by ψ, and ρ/ε_0 replaced by $\operatorname{div} A_0 - g$). Thus, it is possible to satisfy the prescribed conditions on both the curl and divergence of A.

It is easy to see why we have assumed that R is rectangular in this proof, for we must ensure that integrals such as (9.8) and (9.9) are along paths entirely within R, the region in which B is defined.

Note that A is not fully determined in the above proof, since ψ is determined by (9.12) only to within the addition of an arbitrary solution of Laplace's equation. We find, using the uniqueness theorem discussed in §7.2, that apart from a trivial constant of addition, ψ is made unique if $\partial \psi / \partial n$ is specified on the boundary of R. This is equivalent to specifying A_n (the normal component of A) on the boundary, because

$$A_n = (A_0)_n + (\operatorname{grad} \psi)_n = (A_0)_n + \frac{\partial \psi}{\partial n},$$

and $(A_0)_n$ is known. When A_n is specified, the solution of (9.6) is uniquely determined.

EXERCISES

1. Show that if H is the magnetic field of a magnetic dipole, as given in exercise 8, Chapter 4, and if $B = \mu_0 H$, where μ_0 is a constant, then the vector

$$A = \mu_0 \frac{M \wedge r}{4\pi r^3}$$

satisfies the conditions curl $A = B$, div $A = 0$, and hence is the vector potential of B corresponding to the boundary condition $A_r \to 0$ as $r \to \infty$, where A_r denotes the outward radial component of A.

2. From the relation curl $H = j$ for the magnetic field due to a steady volume electric current j (see exercise 9, Chapter 8), show that if curl $A = B = \mu H$, where μ is a constant, and if div $A = 0$, then

$$\nabla^2 A = -\mu j.$$

By considering the three scalar equations obtained by taking rectangular components in this vector equation, show that a particular solution is

$$A(x, y, z) = \frac{\mu}{4\pi} \iiint_{V'} \frac{j(x', y', z') \, dx' dy' dz'}{\{(x-x')^2 + (y-y')^2 + (z-z')^2\}^{\frac{1}{2}}}$$

where V' is the region occupied by the current expressed in primed coordinates. (c.f. equations (6.33), (6.34)).

CHAPTER 10

Orthogonal Curvilinear Coordinate Systems

10.1 Curvilinear Coordinates

The purpose of this chapter is to derive expressions for the ∇ operations in terms of some non-cartesian coordinates. Let u_1, u_2, u_3 be any continuous functions of x, y and z with continuous first derivatives,

$$u_1 = u_1(x,y,z), \qquad u_2 = u_2(x,y,z), \qquad u_3 = u_3(x,y,z). \quad (10.1)$$

The surfaces $u_1 = a$, $u_2 = b$, $u_3 = c$, where a, b, c are constants, are the respective level surfaces of the three functions. Suppose that for each set of values that may be assigned to a, b, c, there is just one point at which the three level surfaces meet, i.e. a unique point is defined whenever a set of values is given to u_1, u_2, u_3. Then u_1, u_2, u_3 may be used as coordinates, in place of x, y, z, to label points of space. They are called *curvilinear coordinates*, since the *coordinate lines* (lines along which only one coordinate varies) are in general curved. The level surfaces of the u's are known as *coordinate surfaces*, and correspond to the coordinate planes in cartesian systems.

Since, by assumption, x, y and z are uniquely determined when values are given to u_1, u_2, u_3, it follows that in principle we may solve (10.1) to give

$$x = x(u_1,u_2,u_3), \qquad y = y(u_1,u_2,u_3), \qquad z = z(u_1,u_2,u_3). \quad (10.2)$$

It is worth noting that a condition that the three level surfaces of the u's through any point P meet at no other point near P is that the normals to the level surfaces are non-coplanar at P. (This condition applies to the normals to any three surfaces which meet at just one point.) In other words, the scalar triple product of the gradients of u_1, u_2, u_3 must be non-zero at P, and so we have the determinantal condition

$$\begin{vmatrix} \dfrac{\partial u_1}{\partial x} & \dfrac{\partial u_1}{\partial y} & \dfrac{\partial u_1}{\partial z} \\[2ex] \dfrac{\partial u_2}{\partial x} & \dfrac{\partial u_2}{\partial y} & \dfrac{\partial u_2}{\partial z} \\[2ex] \dfrac{\partial u_3}{\partial x} & \dfrac{\partial u_3}{\partial y} & \dfrac{\partial u_3}{\partial z} \end{vmatrix} \neq 0, \tag{10.3}$$

which is a well known analytical condition for the set of equations (10.1) to possess a solution, in the form (10.2), near the point P. The determinant (10.3) is called the *Jacobian* of u_1, u_2, u_3 with respect to x, y, z.

Let $\mathbf{r} = x\mathbf{i} + y\mathbf{j} + z\mathbf{k}$, and form the differential at the point P,

$$d\mathbf{r} = \frac{\partial \mathbf{r}}{\partial u_1} du_1 + \frac{\partial \mathbf{r}}{\partial u_2} du_2 + \frac{\partial \mathbf{r}}{\partial u_3} du_3. \tag{10.4}$$

If u_2 and u_3 are kept constant, so that $du_2 = du_3 = 0$, and if $du_1 > 0$, then the differential $d\mathbf{r}$ is in the direction of the tangent to the u_1 coordinate line (in the sense of u_1 increasing). Therefore, the tangent to the u_1 coordinate line is parallel to $\partial \mathbf{r}/\partial u_1$. Similar results apply for the other coordinate lines, and so if $\mathbf{e}_1, \mathbf{e}_2, \mathbf{e}_3$ are unit tangent vectors in the directions u_1, u_2, u_3 increasing, respectively, then

$$\frac{\partial \mathbf{r}}{\partial u_1} = h_1 \mathbf{e}_1, \qquad \frac{\partial \mathbf{r}}{\partial u_2} = h_2 \mathbf{e}_2, \qquad \frac{\partial \mathbf{r}}{\partial u_3} = h_3 \mathbf{e}_3, \tag{10.5}$$

where h_1, h_2, h_3 are certain functions of u_1, u_2, u_3, and are positive. On taking magnitudes in (10.5), we get

$$h_1 = \left| \frac{\partial \mathbf{r}}{\partial u_1} \right|, \qquad h_2 = \left| \frac{\partial \mathbf{r}}{\partial u_2} \right|, \qquad h_3 = \left| \frac{\partial \mathbf{r}}{\partial u_3} \right| \tag{10.6}$$

Again, on substituting for (10.5) in (10.4), we get

$$d\mathbf{r} = h_1 \, du_1 \, \mathbf{e}_1 + h_2 \, du_2 \, \mathbf{e}_2 + h_3 \, du_3 \, \mathbf{e}_3. \tag{10.7}$$

Either of the last two results shows that each $h_i (i = 1, 2, 3)$ is approximately the ratio of the magnitudes of the actual displacement $\Delta \mathbf{r}$ and the coordinate increment Δu_i, for a small displacement along the u_i coordinate line (see Fig. 10.1). The h's are important in what follows, and may be obtained from (10.6) when $\mathbf{r}$ is expressed in terms of the u's, or in some cases from (10.7) and a diagram.

When the coordinate lines intersect orthogonally at each point, the system is known as an *orthogonal curvilinear coordinate system*. In

L

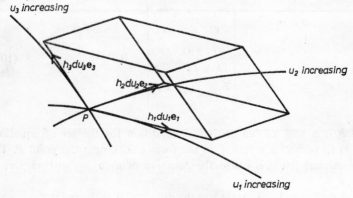

Fig. 10.1

particular, a *right handed* orthogonal curvilinear coordinate system is one in which at each point the vectors e_1, e_2, e_3, in that order, form a right handed set. We shall be concerned only with right handed orthogonal systems in the rest of this chapter.

For orthogonal systems, the square of the 3-dimensional line element (*cf.* (3.17)) $ds^2 = d\mathbf{r} . d\mathbf{r}$ takes an especially simple form. By (10.7), since $e_1 . e_2 = 0$, $e_1 . e_1 = 1$, etc., we have

$$ds^2 = h_1{}^2 du_1{}^2 + h_2{}^2 du_2{}^2 + h_3{}^2 du_3{}^2. \tag{10.8}$$

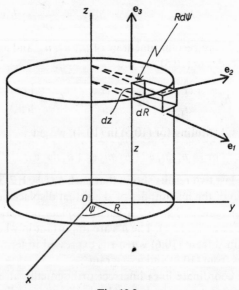

Fig. 10.2

Examples.

(i) *Cylindrical polar coordinates*: By (10.8) and Fig. 10.2,

$$u_1 = R, \quad u_2 = \psi, \quad u_3 = z,$$
$$h_1 = 1, \quad h_2 = R, \quad h_3 = 1,$$
$$ds^2 = dR^2 + R^2 d\psi^2 + dz^2.$$

(ii) *Spherical polar coordinates:* By (10.8) and Fig. 10.3,

$$u_1 = r, \quad u_2 = \theta, \quad u_3 = \psi,$$
$$h_1 = 1, \quad h_2 = r, \quad h_3 = r\sin\theta,$$
$$ds^2 = dr^2 + r^2 d\theta^2 + r^2\sin^2\theta \, d\psi^2.$$

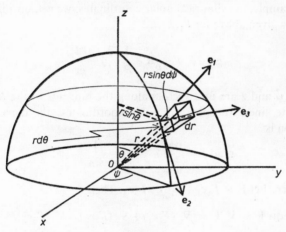

Fig. 10.3

10.2   Nabla Operations

In the following, ϕ and $\mathbf{F}$ are scalar and vector point functions, expressed as functions of orthogonal curvilinear coordinates u_1, u_2, u_3, and are assumed continuous with continuous derivatives as necessary.

Gradient. The resolute of grad ϕ in the direction of $\mathbf{e}_1$ is the rate o change of ϕ with respect to displacements in this direction (directional derivative) and so

$$\mathbf{e}_1 \cdot \operatorname{grad}\phi = \lim_{\Delta u_1 \to 0} \frac{\phi(u_1 + \Delta u_1, u_2, u_3) - \phi(u_1, u_2, u_3)}{h_1 \, \Delta u_1} = \frac{1}{h_1}\frac{\partial\phi}{\partial u_1}$$

since h_1 is independent of Δu_1. Alternatively, we get this result by putting $du_2 = du_3 = 0$, $du_1 > 0$, in (10.7). We have $|d\mathbf{r}| = h_1 du_1$ and

$$\mathbf{e}_1 \cdot \operatorname{grad} \phi = \frac{d\phi}{|d\mathbf{r}|} = \frac{d\phi}{h_1 du_1} = \frac{1}{h_1} \frac{\partial \phi}{\partial u_1},$$

as before. By similar reasoning, it follows that the resolutes of $\operatorname{grad} \phi$ in the directions $\mathbf{e}_2, \mathbf{e}_3$ are respectively

$$\frac{1}{h_2} \frac{\partial \phi}{\partial u_2}, \quad \frac{1}{h_3} \frac{\partial \phi}{\partial u_3},$$

and therefore

$$\operatorname{grad} \phi = \nabla \phi = \frac{1}{h_1} \frac{\partial \phi}{\partial u_1} \mathbf{e}_1 + \frac{1}{h_2} \frac{\partial \phi}{\partial u_2} \mathbf{e}_2 + \frac{1}{h_3} \frac{\partial \phi}{\partial u_3} \mathbf{e}_3. \tag{10.9}$$

For example, in cylindrical polar coordinates, we get, on substituting the values given above for h_1, h_2, h_3,

$$\operatorname{grad} \phi = \frac{\partial \phi}{\partial R} \hat{\mathbf{R}} + \frac{1}{R} \frac{\partial \phi}{\partial \psi} \hat{\boldsymbol{\psi}} + \frac{\partial \phi}{\partial z} \hat{\mathbf{z}}, \tag{10.10}$$

where $\hat{\mathbf{R}}, \hat{\boldsymbol{\psi}}$ and $\hat{\mathbf{z}}$ are unit vectors along the tangents to the R, ψ and z coordinate lines. In spherical polar coordinates, the corresponding expression is

$$\operatorname{grad} \phi = \frac{\partial \phi}{\partial r} \hat{\mathbf{r}} + \frac{1}{r} \frac{\partial \phi}{\partial \theta} \hat{\boldsymbol{\theta}} + \frac{1}{r \sin \theta} \frac{\partial \phi}{\partial \psi} \hat{\boldsymbol{\psi}}. \tag{10.11}$$

Divergence. Let $\mathbf{F} = F_1 \mathbf{e}_1 + F_2 \mathbf{e}_2 + F_3 \mathbf{e}_3$. Then

$$\operatorname{div} \mathbf{F} = \nabla \cdot \mathbf{F} = \nabla \cdot (F_1 \mathbf{e}_1) + \nabla \cdot (F_2 \mathbf{e}_2) + \nabla \cdot (F_3 \mathbf{e}_3). \tag{10.12}$$

Consider

$$\nabla u_1 = \frac{1}{h_1} \frac{\partial u_1}{\partial u_1} \mathbf{e}_1 + \frac{1}{h_2} \frac{\partial u_1}{\partial u_2} \mathbf{e}_2 + \frac{1}{h_3} \frac{\partial u_1}{\partial u_3} \mathbf{e}_3 = \frac{1}{h_1} \mathbf{e}_1.$$

From this equation and two similar equations for $\nabla u_2, \nabla u_3$, we obtain

$$\mathbf{e}_1 = h_1 \nabla u_1, \quad \mathbf{e}_2 = h_2 \nabla u_2, \quad \mathbf{e}_3 = h_3 \nabla u_3. \tag{10.13}$$

But $\mathbf{e}_1 = \mathbf{e}_2 \wedge \mathbf{e}_3$, etc., and so, also

$$\begin{aligned}
\mathbf{e}_1 &= h_2 \nabla u_2 \wedge h_3 \nabla u_3 = h_2 h_3 \nabla u_2 \wedge \nabla u_3, \\
\mathbf{e}_2 &= h_3 h_1 \nabla u_3 \wedge \nabla u_1, \\
\mathbf{e}_3 &= h_1 h_2 \nabla u_1 \wedge \nabla u_2.
\end{aligned} \tag{10.14}$$

Therefore,

$$\nabla.(F_1 e_1) = \nabla.(F_1 h_2 h_3 \nabla u_2 \wedge \nabla u_3)$$
$$= F_1 h_2 h_3 \nabla.(\nabla u_2 \wedge \nabla u_3) + \nabla(F_1 h_2 h_3).(\nabla u_2 \wedge \nabla u_3).$$

By identity (iv) on p. 154,

$$\nabla.(\nabla u_2 \wedge \nabla u_3) = (\nabla u_3).(\nabla \wedge \nabla u_2) - (\nabla u_2).(\nabla \wedge \nabla u_3) = 0,$$

since $\nabla \wedge \nabla u_2 = \nabla \wedge \nabla u_3 = 0$, and

$$\nabla.(F_1 e_1) = \left\{ \frac{1}{h_1} \frac{\partial}{\partial u_1}(F_1 h_2 h_3) e_1 + \ldots \right\}. \frac{e_1}{h_2 h_3}$$
$$= \frac{1}{h_1 h_2 h_3} \frac{\partial}{\partial u_1}(F_1 h_2 h_3),$$

by (10.9) and (10.14). The other two terms in (10.12) can be dealt with in the same way, or, more simply, by cyclic permutation of the indices 1, 2, 3 in the above. Adding the three results then obtained, we get

$$\nabla.F = \frac{1}{h_1 h_2 h_3} \left\{ \frac{\partial}{\partial u_1}(F_1 h_2 h_3) + \frac{\partial}{\partial u_2}(F_2 h_3 h_1) + \frac{\partial}{\partial u_3}(F_3 h_1 h_2) \right\} \quad (10.15)$$

∇^2. By replacing F by grad ϕ, and using (10.9) we obtain an expression for $\nabla^2 \phi$,

$$\nabla^2 \phi = \frac{1}{h_1 h_2 h_3} \left\{ \frac{\partial}{\partial u_1}\left(\frac{h_2 h_3}{h_1} \frac{\partial \phi}{\partial u_1} \right) + \frac{\partial}{\partial u_2}\left(\frac{h_3 h_1}{h_2} \frac{\partial \phi}{\partial u_2} \right) + \frac{\partial}{\partial u_3}\left(\frac{h_1 h_2}{h_3} \frac{\partial \phi}{\partial u_3} \right) \right\}. \quad (10.16)$$

Note. Care must be taken if the operator on the right hand side of (10.16) is used to express $\nabla^2 A$, where A is a given vector, in curvilinear coordinates. We may write

$$\nabla^2 A = \nabla^2(A_x i + A_y j + A_z k) = (\nabla^2 A_x) i + (\nabla^2 A_y) j + (\nabla^2 A_z) k,$$

since i, j, k are constant vectors. If A_x, A_y, A_z are expressed as functions of u_1, u_2, u_3, then (10.16) may be used to evaluate $\nabla^2 A_x$, $\nabla^2 A_y$, $\nabla^2 A_z$ and a valid result is obtained. On the other hand, it is normally much more convenient to work entirely in curvilinear coordinates, and so we need to consider

$$\nabla^2 A = \nabla^2(A_1 e_1 + A_2 e_2 + A_3 e_3).$$

The difficulty here is that derivatives of e_1, e_2 and e_3 have to be evaluated.

It is simplest in practice to avoid this complication entirely, and replace $\nabla^2 \mathbf{A}$ in curvilinear coordinates by means of the identity (8.6)

$$\nabla^2 \mathbf{A} = \operatorname{grad} \operatorname{div} \mathbf{A} - \operatorname{curl} \operatorname{curl} \mathbf{A}.$$

Curl. We have

$$\operatorname{curl} \mathbf{F} = \nabla \wedge \mathbf{F} = \nabla \wedge (F_1 \mathbf{e}_1) + \nabla \wedge (F_2 \mathbf{e}_2) + \nabla \wedge (F_3 \mathbf{e}_3).$$

Now, by (10.13)

$$\nabla \wedge (F_1 \mathbf{e}_1) = \nabla \wedge (F_1 h_1 \nabla u_1) = F_1 h_1 \nabla \wedge \nabla u_1 + \nabla (F_1 h_1) \wedge \nabla u_1.$$

But $\nabla \wedge \nabla u_1 = 0$, and so by (10.9)

$$\nabla \wedge (F_1 \mathbf{e}_1) = \left\{ \frac{1}{h_1} \frac{\partial}{\partial u_1}(F_1 h_1)\mathbf{e}_1 + \frac{1}{h_2} \frac{\partial}{\partial u_2}(F_1 h_1)\mathbf{e}_2 + \frac{1}{h_3} \frac{\partial}{\partial u_3}(F_1 h_1)\mathbf{e}_3 \right\} \wedge \frac{\mathbf{e}_1}{h_1}$$

$$= -\frac{1}{h_2 h_1} \frac{\partial}{\partial u_2}(F_1 h_1)\mathbf{e}_3 + \frac{1}{h_3 h_1} \frac{\partial}{\partial u_3}(F_1 h_1)\mathbf{e}_2.$$

If we write down corresponding results, by cyclic permutation of indices, for $\nabla \wedge (F_2 \mathbf{e}_2)$ and $\nabla \wedge (F_3 \mathbf{e}_3)$ we get on adding the three results,

$$\nabla \wedge \mathbf{F} = \frac{1}{h_2 h_3} \left\{ \frac{\partial}{\partial u_2}(F_3 h_3) - \frac{\partial}{\partial u_3}(F_2 h_2) \right\} \mathbf{e}_1 + \dots$$

$$= \frac{1}{h_1 h_2 h_3} \begin{vmatrix} h_1 \mathbf{e}_1 & h_2 \mathbf{e}_2 & h_3 \mathbf{e}_3 \\ \dfrac{\partial}{\partial u_1} & \dfrac{\partial}{\partial u_2} & \dfrac{\partial}{\partial u_3} \\ h_1 F_1 & h_2 F_2 & h_3 F_3 \end{vmatrix}.$$

Examples. Substitution of appropriate values for h_1, h_2, h_3, etc. into the above formulae leads to the following, as should be verified by the reader:

Cylindrical polar coordinates: ($h_1 = 1$, $h_2 = R$, $h_3 = 1$)

$$\operatorname{grad} \phi = \frac{\partial \phi}{\partial R}\hat{\mathbf{R}} + \frac{1}{R}\frac{\partial \phi}{\partial \psi}\hat{\boldsymbol{\psi}} + \frac{\partial \phi}{\partial z}\hat{\mathbf{z}}$$

$$\operatorname{div} \mathbf{F} = \frac{1}{R}\frac{\partial}{\partial R}(R F_R) + \frac{1}{R}\frac{\partial F_\psi}{\partial \psi} + \frac{\partial F_z}{\partial z}$$

$$\nabla^2 \phi = \frac{1}{R}\frac{\partial}{\partial R}\left(R\frac{\partial \phi}{\partial R} \right) + \frac{1}{R^2}\frac{\partial^2 \phi}{\partial \psi^2} + \frac{\partial^2 \phi}{\partial z^2}$$

$$\text{curl } \mathbf{F} = \frac{1}{R} \begin{vmatrix} \hat{\mathbf{R}} & R\hat{\psi} & \hat{\mathbf{z}} \\ \dfrac{\partial}{\partial R} & \dfrac{\partial}{\partial \psi} & \dfrac{\partial}{\partial z} \\ F_R & RF_\psi & F_z \end{vmatrix}.$$

Spherical polar coordinates: ($h_1 = 1$, $h_2 = r$, $h_3 = r\sin\theta$)

$$\text{grad } \phi = \frac{\partial \phi}{\partial r}\hat{\mathbf{r}} + \frac{1}{r}\frac{\partial \phi}{\partial \theta}\hat{\theta} + \frac{1}{r\sin\theta}\frac{\partial \phi}{\partial \psi}\hat{\psi}$$

$$\text{div } \mathbf{F} = \frac{1}{r^2}\frac{\partial}{\partial r}(r^2 F_r) + \frac{1}{r\sin\theta}\frac{\partial}{\partial \theta}(\sin\theta\, F_\theta) + \frac{1}{r\sin\theta}\frac{\partial F_\psi}{\partial \psi}$$

$$\nabla^2 \phi = \frac{1}{r^2}\frac{\partial}{\partial r}\left(r^2\frac{\partial \phi}{\partial r}\right) + \frac{1}{r^2\sin\theta}\frac{\partial}{\partial \theta}\left(\sin\theta\frac{\partial \phi}{\partial \theta}\right) + \frac{1}{r^2\sin^2\theta}\frac{\partial^2 \phi}{\partial \psi^2}$$

$$\text{curl } \mathbf{F} = \frac{1}{r^2\sin\theta} \begin{vmatrix} \hat{\mathbf{r}} & r\hat{\theta} & r\sin\theta\,\hat{\psi} \\ \dfrac{\partial}{\partial r} & \dfrac{\partial}{\partial \theta} & \dfrac{\partial}{\partial \psi} \\ F_r & rF_\theta & r\sin\theta\, F_\psi \end{vmatrix}.$$

EXERCISES

1. Show that in a cylindrical polar coordinate system the unit vectors $\hat{\mathbf{R}}, \hat{\psi}, \hat{\mathbf{z}}$ are

$$\hat{\mathbf{R}} = \cos\psi\,\mathbf{i} + \sin\psi\,\mathbf{j}, \quad \hat{\psi} = -\sin\psi\,\mathbf{i} + \cos\psi\,\mathbf{j}, \quad \hat{\mathbf{z}} = \mathbf{k}.$$

Hence show by solving that

$$\mathbf{i} = \cos\psi\,\hat{\mathbf{R}} - \sin\psi\,\hat{\psi}, \quad \mathbf{j} = \sin\psi\,\hat{\mathbf{R}} + \cos\psi\,\hat{\psi}, \quad \mathbf{k} = \hat{\mathbf{z}}.$$

Express the vector $\mathbf{F} = 2\mathbf{i} + z\mathbf{j} + x\mathbf{k}$ in terms of cylindrical coordinates and the vectors $\hat{\mathbf{R}}, \hat{\psi}, \hat{\mathbf{z}}$. (Note that $\mathbf{r} = x\mathbf{i} + y\mathbf{j} + z\mathbf{k} = R\cos\psi\,\mathbf{i} + R\sin\psi\,\mathbf{j} + z\mathbf{k}$, and

$$\hat{\mathbf{R}} = \frac{\partial \mathbf{r}}{\partial R}\bigg/ \left|\frac{\partial \mathbf{r}}{\partial R}\right|, \text{ etc.})$$

Repeat the exercise using spherical polar coordinates, and the unit vectors $\hat{\mathbf{r}}, \hat{\theta}, \hat{\psi}$, in place of cylindrical coordinates.

2. Show that in *parabolic cylindrical coordinates* u, v, z, where $x = \frac{1}{2}(u^2 - v^2)$, $y = uv$ ($-\infty < u < \infty$, $v \geqslant 0$, $-\infty < z < \infty$), the 3-dimensional line element ds is given by

$$ds^2 \equiv d\mathbf{r}.d\mathbf{r} = (u^2 + v^2)(du^2 + dv^2) + dz^2.$$

Show that in *prolate spheroidal coordinates* α, β, ψ, where $x = \sinh\alpha\sin\beta\cos\psi$, $y = \sinh\alpha\sin\beta\sin\psi$, $z = \cosh\alpha\cos\beta$ ($\alpha \geqslant 0, 0 \leqslant \beta \leqslant \pi, 0 \leqslant \psi < 2\pi$), the line element is given by

$$ds^2 = (\sinh^2\alpha + \sin^2\beta)(d\alpha^2 + d\beta^2) + \sinh^2\alpha\sin^2\beta\, d\psi^2.$$

3.   Prove that if u_1, u_2, u_3 are (right handed) orthogonal curvilinear coordinates, then

$$\begin{vmatrix} \dfrac{\partial x}{\partial u_1} & \dfrac{\partial x}{\partial u_2} & \dfrac{\partial x}{\partial u_3} \\[2mm] \dfrac{\partial y}{\partial u_1} & \dfrac{\partial y}{\partial u_2} & \dfrac{\partial y}{\partial u_3} \\[2mm] \dfrac{\partial z}{\partial u_1} & \dfrac{\partial z}{\partial u_2} & \dfrac{\partial z}{\partial u_3} \end{vmatrix} = h_1 h_2 h_3,$$

in the notation of (10.5).

4.   Use the expressions (§ 10.2) for $\nabla^2\phi$ in cylindrical polar and spherical polar coordinates to obtain the most general form of expression for the electrostatic potential in empty space (i) in a system possessing cylindrical symmetry (i.e. $\phi = \phi(R)$), (ii) in a system possessing spherical symmetry ($\phi = \phi(r)$). Verify the results by use of Gauss's law.

CHAPTER 11

Summary of Formulae

For reference purposes, some of the most important formulae in vector field theory are listed below. Except for one or two ∇ identities, which have been set as exercises, they have all been derived in the text. Unless otherwise stated, all scalars and vectors appearing in the formulae are assumed to be continuous point functions and to have continuous partial derivatives up to the highest order occurring. As usual, $\mathbf{r}$ denotes $x\mathbf{i} + y\mathbf{j} + z\mathbf{k}$.

Nabla operator

Nabla, or **del**, is the operator (in cartesian coordinates)

$$\nabla = \mathbf{i}\frac{\partial}{\partial x} + \mathbf{j}\frac{\partial}{\partial y} + \mathbf{k}\frac{\partial}{\partial z}.$$

Nabla operations (cartesian coordinates)

$$\operatorname{grad}\phi = \quad \nabla\phi = \mathbf{i}\frac{\partial\phi}{\partial x} + \mathbf{j}\frac{\partial\phi}{\partial y} + \mathbf{k}\frac{\partial\phi}{\partial z}$$

$$\operatorname{div}\mathbf{F} = \quad \nabla\cdot\mathbf{F} = \frac{\partial F_x}{\partial x} + \frac{\partial F_y}{\partial y} + \frac{\partial F_z}{\partial z}$$

$$\nabla^2\phi = \nabla\cdot\nabla\phi = \frac{\partial^2\phi}{\partial x^2} + \frac{\partial^2\phi}{\partial y^2} + \frac{\partial^2\phi}{\partial z^2}$$

$$\nabla^2\mathbf{F} = \mathbf{i}\nabla^2 F_x + \mathbf{j}\nabla^2 F_y + \mathbf{k}\nabla^2 F_z$$

$$\operatorname{curl}\mathbf{F} = \quad \nabla\wedge\mathbf{F} = \begin{vmatrix} \mathbf{i} & \mathbf{j} & \mathbf{k} \\ \dfrac{\partial}{\partial x} & \dfrac{\partial}{\partial y} & \dfrac{\partial}{\partial z} \\ F_x & F_y & F_z \end{vmatrix}$$

For a scalar ϕ, the differential $d\phi$ corresponding to a differential displacement $d\mathbf{r}$ is

$$d\phi = \frac{\partial \phi}{\partial x}dx + \frac{\partial \phi}{\partial y}dy + \frac{\partial \phi}{\partial z}dz = \nabla \phi . d\mathbf{r}.$$

The **directional derivative** of ϕ in the direction $\hat{\mathbf{a}}$ is the scalar

$$\hat{\mathbf{a}} . \nabla \phi = a_x \frac{\partial \phi}{\partial x} + a_y \frac{\partial \phi}{\partial y} + a_z \frac{\partial \phi}{\partial z},$$

and an allied quantity for a vector function $\mathbf{b}$ is

$$\hat{\mathbf{a}} . \nabla \mathbf{b} \equiv (\hat{\mathbf{a}} . \nabla)\mathbf{b} = (\hat{\mathbf{a}} . \nabla b_x)\mathbf{i} + (\hat{\mathbf{a}} . \nabla b_y)\mathbf{j} + (\hat{\mathbf{a}} . \nabla b_z)\mathbf{k}.$$

Nabla identities

(i) $\nabla(\phi\psi) = \phi \nabla\psi + \psi \nabla\phi,$

(ii) $\nabla . (\phi\mathbf{F}) = \phi\nabla . \mathbf{F} + (\nabla\phi) . \mathbf{F},$

(iii) $\nabla . (\nabla \wedge \mathbf{F}) = 0,$

(iv) $\nabla . (\mathbf{A} \wedge \mathbf{B}) = \mathbf{B} . (\nabla \wedge \mathbf{A}) - \mathbf{A} . (\nabla \wedge \mathbf{B}),$

(v) $\nabla \wedge (\phi\mathbf{F}) = \phi\nabla \wedge \mathbf{F} + (\nabla\phi) \wedge \mathbf{F},$

(vi) $\nabla \wedge \nabla\phi = 0,$

(vii) $\nabla \wedge (\nabla \wedge \mathbf{F}) = \nabla(\nabla . \mathbf{F}) - \nabla^2\mathbf{F},$

(viii) $\nabla(\mathbf{A} . \mathbf{B}) = (\mathbf{A} . \nabla)\mathbf{B} + (\mathbf{B} . \nabla)\mathbf{A} + \mathbf{A} \wedge (\nabla \wedge \mathbf{B}) + \mathbf{B} \wedge (\nabla \wedge \mathbf{A}),$

(ix) $\nabla \wedge (\mathbf{A} \wedge \mathbf{B}) = (\nabla . \mathbf{B})\mathbf{A} - (\nabla . \mathbf{A})\mathbf{B} + (\mathbf{B} . \nabla)\mathbf{A} - (\mathbf{A} . \nabla)\mathbf{B}.$

(x) $\mathbf{A} \wedge (\nabla \wedge \mathbf{A}) = \frac{1}{2}\nabla A^2 - (\mathbf{A} . \nabla)\mathbf{A}.$

Integral theorems

The **tangential line integral** (T.L.I.) of a vector $\mathbf{F}$ along a curve C is the integral

$$\int_C \mathbf{F} . d\mathbf{r} = \int_C (F_x dx + F_y dy + F_z dz).$$

If $\int_A^B \mathbf{F} . d\mathbf{r}$ is independent of the path joining any two points A and B in a region R, then $\oint_C \mathbf{F} . d\mathbf{r} = 0$ for every closed curve C in R, and conversely.

A necessary and sufficient condition for the T.L.I. $\int_A^B \mathbf{F} . d\mathbf{r}$ to be independent of the path joining points A and B, in a region R, is that $\mathbf{F}$ be the gradient of a single valued scalar function everywhere in R.

The **normal surface integral** of a vector $\mathbf{F}$ over a surface S, with unit normal $\hat{\mathbf{n}}$, is the integral

$$\int_S \mathbf{F}.d\mathbf{S} = \int_S (\mathbf{F}.\hat{\mathbf{n}})\, dS.$$

This is also called the **flux** of $\mathbf{F}$ through S. For closed surfaces, the outward drawn normal is to be taken; otherwise, the sense of direction of $\hat{\mathbf{n}}$ must be specified.

The **solid angle** subtended at a point O, by a differential surface element dS which is located at the point $\mathbf{r}$ relative to O, is

$$\frac{\mathbf{r}.\hat{\mathbf{n}}\, dS}{r^3},$$

where $\hat{\mathbf{n}}$ is the unit normal to dS, and will depend on the sense of direction assigned to $\hat{\mathbf{n}}$. The **magnitude** of the solid angle is the area intercepted on the unit sphere centred at O by the cone of lines from O to the boundary of dS.

Gauss's divergence theorem. If S is a closed surface enclosing a region V, and $\mathbf{F}$ is a vector point function which is continuous and has continuous first partial derivatives in V and on S, then

$$\int_S \mathbf{F}.d\mathbf{S} = \int_V \operatorname{div}\mathbf{F}\, dV,$$

where $d\mathbf{S}$ points away from V. It follows that a formula for the divergence of a vector $\mathbf{F}$, at any point P, is

$$\operatorname{div}\mathbf{F} = \lim_{\Delta V \to 0} \frac{1}{\Delta V} \int \mathbf{F}.d\mathbf{S},$$

where the integration is over the boundary of the elementary volume ΔV which contains P.

Green's first theorem, obtained by putting $\mathbf{F} = \phi\, \nabla\psi$ in Gauss's theorem, is the identity

$$\int_S \phi\frac{\partial\psi}{\partial n}\, dS = \int_V \{\phi\, \nabla^2\psi + (\nabla\phi).(\nabla\psi)\}\, dV.$$

Green's second theorem, obtained by putting $\mathbf{F} = \phi\, \nabla\psi - \psi\, \nabla\phi$ in Gauss's theorem, is the identity

$$\int_S \left(\phi\frac{\partial\psi}{\partial n} - \psi\frac{\partial\phi}{\partial n}\right) dS = \int_V (\phi\, \nabla^2\psi - \psi\, \nabla^2\phi)\, dV.$$

In each of the above, $\partial/\partial n$ denotes rate of change along the outward normal direction, and ϕ and ψ are assumed to have continuous second derivatives.

Stokes's theorem. If S is an open surface bounded by the closed curve C, and if $\mathbf{F}$ is continuous and has continuous first partial derivatives in S and on C, then

$$\oint_C \mathbf{F}.d\mathbf{r} = \int_S \text{curl } \mathbf{F}.d\mathbf{S},$$

where C is described positively with respect to the direction of $d\mathbf{S}$.

It follows that a formula for the resolute of the curl of a vector $\mathbf{F}$ in the direction $\hat{\mathbf{n}}$, at any point P, is

$$\hat{\mathbf{n}}.\text{curl } \mathbf{F} = \lim_{\Delta S \to 0} \frac{1}{\Delta S} \oint \mathbf{F}.d\mathbf{r},$$

where the integration is around the boundary of the surface element ΔS, with normal $\hat{\mathbf{n}}$ and containing P, and the boundary is described positively with respect to the direction of $\hat{\mathbf{n}}$.

Orthogonal curvilinear coordinates

For reasons of space, formulae are not reproduced here. General formulae are to be found on pp. 145 to 150, and those relating to cylindrical polar and spherical polar coordinates on pp. 147, 150 and 151.

Differentials

A.1 Differentials

A function $f(x)$, defined in the neighbourhood of a point x, is *differentiable* at this point if the increment Δf in f corresponding to an arbitrary increment in x can be written

$$\Delta f = A\,\Delta x + \varepsilon\,\Delta x, \tag{A.1}$$

where $\varepsilon \to 0$ as $\Delta x \to 0$, and A is independent of Δx.

Thus, Δf consists of two parts. One is proportional to Δx, and is called the *principal part* of Δf, and the other is a term which tends to zero *faster* than Δx, as $\Delta x \to 0$. If $\Delta x \neq 0$, on dividing by Δx we get

$$\lim_{\Delta x \to 0} \frac{\Delta f}{\Delta x} = A,$$

and so A is simply the derivative $f'(x)$ of f with respect to x. The principal part of Δf is also called the *differential* of f, and is denoted by df,

$$df = f'(x)\,\Delta x.$$

In particular, for the function $f \equiv x$, we have

$$dx = 1.\,\Delta x = \Delta x,$$

and on dividing the differential of f by that of x, we get

$$\frac{df}{dx} = f'(x). \tag{A.2}$$

It is important to realize that the left hand side denotes the ratio of two finite quantities df and dx, and does not involve a limiting process. The equation shows that this ratio is equal to the derivative of f with respect to x, i.e. $(d/dx)f$, which *does* involve a limiting process. However, because df and dx are finite in (A.2), it is permissible to separate them and write

$$df = f'(x)\,dx.$$

This would not be possible if df/dx simply denoted

$$\frac{d}{dx}(f) \equiv \lim_{\Delta x \to 0} \frac{\Delta f}{\Delta x}.$$

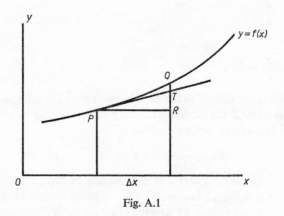

Fig. A.1

In Fig. (A.1), P and Q are the points (x, f), $(x + \Delta x, f + \Delta f)$ on the curve $y = f(x)$, and PT is the tangent to the curve at P. We have $PR = \Delta x = dx$, $RQ = \Delta f$, $RT = df$. Therefore, while Δf is the y displacement from R to the curve, df is the y displacement from R to the tangent PT.

This concept generalizes to functions of several variables. The case where there are three independent variables is considered next.

Definition. A function $f(x, y, z)$ defined in the neighbourhood of a point (x, y, z) is *differentiable* at this point if the increment Δf in f corresponding to arbitrary increments Δx, Δy, Δz in x, y and z can be written

$$\Delta f = A\,\Delta x + B\,\Delta y + C\,\Delta z + \varepsilon\rho,$$

where ρ denotes $|\Delta x| + |\Delta y| + |\Delta z|$, $\varepsilon \to 0$ as $\rho \to 0$, and A, B, C are independent of Δx, Δy and Δz.

If $\Delta y = \Delta z = 0$ and $\Delta x \neq 0$, then

$$\frac{\Delta f}{\Delta x} = A + \varepsilon\frac{|\Delta x|}{\Delta x}.$$

If Δx is allowed to tend to zero, then by hypothesiss, $\varepsilon \to 0$, and so

$$\lim_{\Delta x \to 0} \frac{\Delta f}{\Delta x} = A.$$

By definition, this limit is equal to $\partial f/\partial x$, and from this and two similar results involving B and C, we conclude that a differentiable function always possesses first partial derivatives, and that

$$A = \frac{\partial f}{\partial x}, \qquad B = \frac{\partial f}{\partial y}, \qquad C = \frac{\partial f}{\partial z}.$$

The *principal part* of Δf is defined to be

$$df = \frac{\partial f}{\partial x} \Delta x + \frac{\partial f}{\partial y} \Delta y + \frac{\partial f}{\partial z} \Delta z, \qquad (A.3)$$

and is also called the *differential* (or sometimes the *total differential*) of f. In particular, by considering in turn the differentials of the functions x, y and z, we get

$$dx = \Delta x, \qquad dy = \Delta y, \qquad dz = \Delta z,$$

and

$$df = \frac{\partial f}{\partial x} dx + \frac{\partial f}{\partial y} dy + \frac{\partial f}{\partial z} dz. \qquad (A.4)$$

This exact relation should be compared with (but not confused with) the approximate relation

$$\Delta f \simeq \frac{\partial f}{\partial x} \Delta x + \frac{\partial f}{\partial y} \Delta y + \frac{\partial f}{\partial z} \Delta z.$$

It may be shown that any continuous function possessing continuous first partial derivatives is differentiable.

A.2 Relation with Line Integration

Suppose that the formerly independent variables x, y and z are now made to depend on a single independent variable t, so that $x = x(t)$, $y = y(t)$, $z = z(t)$, in some range $t_0 \leqslant t \leqslant t_1$. Then as t increases from t_0 to t_1, the point (x, y, z) describes a space curve C. The function $f(x, y, z)$ is a function of t at points on C,

$$f = f(x(t), y(t), z(t)).$$

We shall assume that $x'(t)$, $y'(t)$, $z'(t)$ exist and are continuous. Corresponding to a differential $dt = \Delta t$, we have by (A.2)

$$dx = x'(t) \, dt, \qquad dy = y'(t) \, dt, \qquad dz = z'(t) \, dt.$$

But, according to a chain rule for differentiation,

$$\frac{df}{dt} = \frac{\partial f}{\partial x}x'(t) + \frac{\partial f}{\partial y}y'(t) + \frac{\partial f}{\partial z}z'(t), \qquad (A.5)$$

and so on multiplying by dt we again get (A.4), which shows that (A.4) is valid even though x, y and z are not independent variables. We can integrate (A.5) with respect to t, obtaining

$$\int_{t_0}^{t_1}\frac{df}{dt}\,dt = \int_{t_0}^{t_1}\frac{\partial f}{\partial x}x'(t)\,dt + \int_{t_0}^{t_1}\frac{\partial f}{\partial y}y'(t)\,dt + \int_{t_0}^{t_1}\frac{\partial f}{\partial z}z'(t)\,dt. \quad (A.6)$$

Let A and B be the initial and terminal points of C. By elementary rules of calculus for the change of variable in an integral, we have that if x increases or decreases monotonically with t in $t_0 \leqslant t \leqslant t_1$, then

$$\int_{t_0}^{t_1}\frac{\partial f}{\partial x}x'(t)\,dt = \int_{A}^{B}\frac{\partial f}{\partial x}\,dx,$$

where in the last integral x is used as a parameter along C, and the notation A and B is used to signify that the limits are to be the initial and final values of the integration variable on C. If y, z and f are monotonic functions of t, also, in $t_0 \leqslant t \leqslant t_1$, then the other integrals in (A.6) can be dealt with in a similar way, and we get

$$\int_{A}^{B} df = \int_{A}^{B}\frac{\partial f}{\partial x}\,dx + \int_{A}^{B}\frac{\partial f}{\partial y}\,dy + \int_{A}^{B}\frac{\partial f}{\partial z}\,dz$$

$$= \int_{A}^{B}\left(\frac{\partial f}{\partial x}\,dx + \frac{\partial f}{\partial y}\,dy + \frac{\partial f}{\partial z}\,dz\right). \qquad (A.7)$$

When the above conditions of monotonic behaviour do not apply over the whole curve, one can usually divide the curve into segments, in each of which the conditions are satisfied. Then the whole curve is treated by summing the individual relations of the form (A.7) which apply to each segment.

The importance of this derivation of (A.7) is that it shows how the equation (A.4) involving differentials may be integrated by introducing a path of integration. The value of the integral will depend only on the values of f at the end points A and B, and not on the path joining them, for

$$\int_{A}^{B} df = \left|f\right|_{A}^{B}.$$

One may also integrate expressions of the form

$$P(x,y,z)\,dx + Q(x,y,z)\,dy + R(x,y,z)\,dz \qquad (A.8)$$

along a specified path, where P, Q and R are continuous functions of x, y, z. But, in general,

$$\int_{\substack{A \\ C}}^{B} (P\,dx + Q\,dy + R\,dz)$$

will depend on the curve C, and not merely on its end points A, B. If P, Q and R have continuous first partial derivatives, the condition that the integral is independent of the path between given end points in a simply connected region is that the vector function $P\mathbf{i} + Q\mathbf{j} + R\mathbf{k}$ has vanishing curl in the region (Chapter 9), i.e. that

$$\frac{\partial P}{\partial y} = \frac{\partial Q}{\partial x}, \qquad \frac{\partial P}{\partial z} = \frac{\partial R}{\partial x}, \qquad \frac{\partial Q}{\partial z} = \frac{\partial R}{\partial y}.$$

In this case, (A.8) is said to be an *exact differential*, and there exists a function $f(x, y, z)$ such that

$$df = P\,dx + Q\,dy + R\,dz,$$

whence

$$P = \frac{\partial f}{\partial x}, \qquad Q = \frac{\partial f}{\partial y}, \qquad R = \frac{\partial f}{\partial z},$$

i.e. $P\mathbf{i} + Q\mathbf{j} + R\mathbf{k} = \operatorname{grad} f$. This is proved in the theorem on p. 138.

ANSWERS TO EXERCISES

Chapter 1

1. (i) $3\mathbf{i}+2\mathbf{j}-\mathbf{k}$, (ii) $-3\mathbf{i}-6\mathbf{j}+3\mathbf{k}$, (iii) $-9\mathbf{i}-5\mathbf{j}+4\mathbf{k}$. $-2\mathbf{i}-6\mathbf{j}+3\mathbf{k}$.

2. $(\mathbf{i}+4\mathbf{j}-\mathbf{k})/3\sqrt{2}$.

3. (i) $\sqrt{(34)}$, $\sqrt{(34)}$, $\sqrt{(110)}$, (ii) $(3/\sqrt{(34)}, 0, -5/\sqrt{(34)})$, $(-3/\sqrt{(34)}, 0, 5/\sqrt{(34)})$, $(9/\sqrt{(110)}, 2/\sqrt{(110)}, 5/\sqrt{(110)})$.

7. $\pi-\cos^{-1}(1/3\sqrt{3})$.

8. (i) $2(2\mathbf{i}-4\mathbf{j}-5\mathbf{k})$, or $6\sqrt{5}$ units in the direction of the vector $2\mathbf{i}-4\mathbf{j}-5\mathbf{k}$, (ii) $4(2\mathbf{i}-\mathbf{k})$, or $4\sqrt{5}$ units in the direction of the vector $2\mathbf{i}-\mathbf{k}$.

10. 29, $29\mathbf{i}-\mathbf{j}+19\mathbf{k}$, $-3\mathbf{i}-3\mathbf{j}+4\mathbf{k}$.

11. $\pm(3\mathbf{i}-\mathbf{j}-4\mathbf{k})/\sqrt{(26)}$, $\mathbf{r}\cdot(3\mathbf{i}-\mathbf{j}-4\mathbf{k}) = -5, 5/\sqrt{(26)}$.

13. $(\mathbf{r}-\mathbf{a})\cdot\{(\mathbf{a}-\mathbf{a}')\wedge\mathbf{b}\} = 0$.

16. ($F \equiv$ false, $T \equiv$ true) (i) F, (ii) T, (iii) F, (iv) T, (v) F, (vi) F, (vii) T, (viii) T, (ix) T, (x) T, (xi) F, (xii) T, (xiii) F, (xiv) T, (xv) T, (xvi) T.

Chapter 2

1. (i) $e^u\mathbf{i}+2u\mathbf{j}-(2u+1)e^{2u}\mathbf{k}$, (ii) $-(2u+1)e^{2u}$, (iii) $2u(1-2u-2u^2)e^{2u}\mathbf{i}+(3u+4)e^{3u}\mathbf{j}+(2-u^2)e^u\mathbf{k}$.

2. (i) $t\cos t-\sin t$, (ii) $\mathbf{k}$, (iii) $t(t\cos t+2\sin t)$.

3. $a(-\sin t\,\mathbf{i}+\cos t\,\mathbf{j})+b\mathbf{k}$, $-a(\cos t\,\mathbf{i}+\sin t\,\mathbf{j})$.

4. $\mathbf{i}, x/r$.

5. $(\mathbf{a}\wedge\mathbf{b})\cdot(\dot{\mathbf{a}}\wedge\mathbf{b}+\mathbf{a}\wedge\dot{\mathbf{b}})/|\mathbf{a}\wedge\mathbf{b}|$.

7. $\mathbf{i}\cos nt+\mathbf{j}(\sin nt)/n$.

9. (i) $\mathbf{a}\wedge\dot{\mathbf{r}}+\mathbf{c}$, (ii) $\dot{\mathbf{r}}\wedge\ddot{\mathbf{r}}+\mathbf{c}$, (iii) $\dot{\mathbf{r}}+\mathbf{c}$, where $\mathbf{c}$ is an arbitrary constant vector.

10. $(e-1)\mathbf{i}+\frac{1}{3}\mathbf{j}-\frac{1}{4}(e^2+1)\mathbf{k}$.

Chapter 3

1. $\frac{7}{10}$.

2. $\frac{1}{4}e(e^{15}-1)$.

3. $-2a^3$ units.

4. -8; $f = x^2y^2-\frac{3}{4}z^4$.

5. (i) $\frac{1}{10}\mathbf{i}+\frac{2}{11}\mathbf{j}+\frac{1}{4}\mathbf{k}$, (ii) $\frac{16}{3}$.

7. (i) 3, (ii) $4\pi a^3$.

8. -15.

10. $\frac{3}{2}\pi$.

11. $\frac{2}{3}\pi a^3(2\mathbf{i}+\mathbf{k})$.

12. $\hat{\mathbf{t}}_1 = (1+3\sin^2u)^{-\frac{1}{2}}(\cos u\cos v, \cos u\sin v, -2\sin u)$,
$\hat{\mathbf{t}}_2 = (-\sin v, \cos v, 0)$; $ds^2 = (1+3\sin^2u)\,du^2+\sin^2u\,dv^2$; $\pi(4\pi\sqrt{3}+9)/36$.

13. (i) $\frac{1}{2}\mathbf{i}-2\mathbf{j}+2\mathbf{k}$,   (ii) $-18\pi\mathbf{j}$,   (iii) 0.

Chapter 4

1. $3\mathbf{i}+2\mathbf{j}+12\mathbf{k}$.

2. $-4/\sqrt{6}$.

3. (i) $x\hat{\mathbf{r}}+r\mathbf{i}$,   (ii) $(\cos r)\hat{\mathbf{r}}$,   (iii) $e^{\sin r}(\cos r)\hat{\mathbf{r}}$.

4. $-\frac{1}{2}a\sqrt{(10)}$.

7. $\phi = y(z^{-1}xe^x+1)+C$, where C is an arbitrary constant.

9. $\nabla\phi\wedge(\mathbf{F}\wedge\nabla\phi)/(\nabla\phi)^2$.

10. $12x-4y-z = 0$.

Chapter 6

1. -18.

2. 2.

6. $\frac{405}{2}\pi$.

8. $-\pi a^2$, if $d\mathbf{S}$ is directed away from the origin.

10. (i) $A\ln(x^2+y^2)+B$,   (ii) $A\tan^{-1}(y/x)+B$,   (iii) $A\{\ln(x^2+y^2)+z\}+B$.

Chapter 8

2. $\phi = x^2yz$.

3. $-\pi a^2$.

Chapter 10

1. $\mathbf{F} = (2\cos\psi+z\sin\psi)\hat{\mathbf{R}}+(z\cos\psi-2\sin\psi)\hat{\boldsymbol{\psi}}+R\cos\psi\,\hat{\mathbf{z}}$,
$\mathbf{F} = \sin\theta\{2\cos\psi+r\cos\theta(\sin\psi+\cos\psi)\}\hat{\mathbf{r}}+\{2\cos\theta\cos\psi$
$\qquad\qquad +r(\cos^2\theta\sin\psi-\sin^2\theta\cos\psi)\}\hat{\boldsymbol{\theta}}+(r\cos\theta\cos\psi-2\sin\psi)\hat{\boldsymbol{\psi}}$.

4. (i) $\phi = A\ln R+B$,   (ii) $\phi = (A/r)+B$, where A and B are arbitrary constants.

INDEX